Dylan Thomas
Miscellany Two

Dylan Thomas Miscellany Two

A Visit to Grandpa's
and other stories and poems

J. M. Dent & Sons Ltd
London

Made in Great Britain
at the
Aldine Press · Letchworth · Herts
for J. M. DENT & SONS LTD
Aldine House · Albemarle Street · London

Hardback ISBN 0 460 04174 6
Paperback ISBN 0 460 02049 8

This selection first published (paperbound) 1966
    Reprinted 1971, 1973, 1974
Hardbound edition 1973
    Reprinted 1974

CONTENTS

v

Part I

POEMS

Altarwise by owl-light

I

Altarwise by owl-light in the half-way house
The gentleman lay graveward with his furies;
Abaddon in the hangnail cracked from Adam,
And, from his fork, a dog among the fairies,
The atlas-eater with a jaw for news,
Bit out the mandrake with tomorrow's scream.
Then, penny-eyed, that gentleman of wounds,
Old cock from nowheres and the heaven's egg,
With bones unbuttoned to the half-way winds,
Hatched from the windy salvage on one leg,
Scraped at my cradle in a walking word
That night of time under the Christward shelter:
I am the long world's gentleman, he said,
And share my bed with Capricorn and Cancer.

II

Death is all metaphors, shape in one history;
The child that sucketh long is shooting up,
The planet-ducted pelican of circles
Weans on an artery the gender's strip;
Child of the short spark in a shapeless country
Soon sets alight a long stick from the cradle;
The horizontal cross-bones of Abaddon,
You by the cavern over the black stairs,
Rung bone and blade, the verticals of Adam,
And, manned by midnight, Jacob to the stars.
Hairs of your head, then said the hollow agent,

3

Are but the roots of nettles and of feathers
Over these groundworks thrusting through a pavement
And hemlock-headed in the wood of weathers.

III

First there was the lamb on knocking knees
And three dead seasons on a climbing grave
That Adam's wether in the flock of horns,
Butt of the tree-tailed worm that mounted Eve,
Horned down with skullfoot and the skull of toes
On thunderous pavements in the garden time;
Rip of the vaults, I took my marrow-ladle
Out of the wrinkled undertaker's van,
And, Rip Van Winkle from a timeless cradle,
Dipped me breast-deep in the descended bone;
The black ram, shuffling of the year, old winter,
Alone alive among his mutton fold,
We rung our weathering changes on the ladder,
Said the antipodes, and twice spring chimed.

IV

What is the metre of the dictionary?
The size of genesis? the short spark's gender?
Shade without shape? the shape of Pharaoh's echo?
(My shape of age nagging the wounded whisper).
Which sixth of wind blew out the burning gentry?
(Questions are hunchbacks to the poker marrow).
What of a bamboo man among your acres?
Corset the boneyards for a crooked boy?
Button your bodice on a hump of splinters,

4

My camel's eyes will needle through the shroud.
Love's reflection of the mushroom features,
Stills snapped by night in the bread-sided field,
Once close-up smiling in the wall of pictures,
Arc-lamped thrown back upon the cutting flood.

V

And from the windy West came two-gunned Gabriel,
From Jesu's sleeve trumped up the king of spots,
The sheath-decked jacks, queen with a shuffled heart;
Said the fake gentleman in suit of spades,
Black-tongued and tipsy from salvation's bottle.
Rose my Byzantine Adam in the night.
For loss of blood I fell on Ishmael's plain,
Under the milky mushrooms slew my hunger,
A climbing sea from Asia had me down
And Jonah's Moby snatched me by the hair,
Cross-stroked salt Adam to the frozen angel
Pin-legged on pole-hills with a black medusa
By waste seas where the white bear quoted Virgil
And sirens singing from our lady's sea-straw.

VI

Cartoon of slashes on the tide-traced crater,
He in a book of water tallow-eyed
By lava's light split through the oyster vowels
And burned sea silence on a wick of words.
Pluck, cock, my sea eye, said medusa's scripture,
Lop, love, my fork tongue, said the pin-hilled nettle;
And love plucked out the stinging siren's eye,

5

Old cock from nowheres lopped the minstrel tongue
Till tallow I blew from the wax's tower
The fats of midnight when the salt was singing;
Adam, time's joker, on a witch of cardboard
Spelt out the seven seas, an evil index,
The bagpipe-breasted ladies in the deadweed
Blew out the blood gauze through the wound of manwax.

VII

Now stamp the Lord's Prayer on a grain of rice,
A Bible-leaved of all the written woods
Strip to this tree: a rocking alphabet,
Genesis on the root, the scarecrow word,
And one light's language in the book of trees.
Doom on deniers at the wind-turned statement.
Time's tune my ladies with the teats of music,
The scaled sea-sawers, fix in a naked sponge
Who sucks the bell-voiced Adam out of magic,
Time, milk, and magic, from the world beginning.
Time is the tune my ladies lend their heartbreak,
From bald pavilions and the house of bread
Time tracks the sound of shape on man and cloud,
On rose and icicle the ringing handprint.

VIII

This was the crucifixion on the mountain,
Time's nerve in vinegar, the gallow grave
As tarred with blood as the bright thorns I wept;
The world's my wound, God's Mary in her grief,
Bent like three trees and bird-papped through her shift,

6

With pins for teardrops is the long wound's woman.
This was the sky, Jack Christ, each minstrel angle
Drove in the heaven-driven of the nails
Till the three-coloured rainbow from my nipples
From pole to pole leapt round the snail-waked world
I by the tree of thieves, all glory's sawbones,
Unsex the skeleton this mountain minute,
And by this blowclock witness of the sun
Suffer the heaven's children through my heartbeat.

IX

From the oracular archives and the parchment,
Prophets and fibre kings in oil and letter,
The lamped calligrapher, the queen in splints,
Buckle to lint and cloth their natron footsteps,
Draw on the glove of prints, dead Cairo's henna
Pour like a halo on the caps and serpents.
This was the resurrection in the desert,
Death from a bandage, rants the mask of scholars
Gold on such features, and the linen spirit
Weds my long gentleman to dusts and furies;
With priest and pharaoh bed my gentle wound,
World in the sand, on the triangle landscape,
With stones of odyssey for ash and garland
And rivers of the dead around my neck.

X

Let the tale's sailor from a Christian voyage
Atlaswise hold half-way off the dummy bay
Time's ship-racked gospel on the globe I balance:

So shall winged harbours through the rockbirds' eyes
Spot the blown word, and on the seas I image
December's thorn screwed in a brow of holly.
Let the first Peter from a rainbow's quayrail
Ask the tall fish swept from the bible east,
What rhubarb man peeled in her foam-blue channel
Has sown a flying garden round that sea-ghost?
Green as beginning, let the garden diving
Soar, with its two bark towers, to that Day
When the worm builds with the gold straws of venom
My nest of mercies in the rude, red tree.

After the funeral

(IN MEMORY OF ANN JONES)

After the funeral, mule praises, brays,
Windshake of sailshaped ears, muffle-toed tap
Tap happily of one peg in the thick
Grave's foot, blinds down the lids, the teeth in black,
The spittled eyes, the salt ponds in the sleeves,
Morning smack of the spade that wakes up sleep,
Shakes a desolate boy who slits his throat
In the dark of the coffin and sheds dry leaves,
That breaks one bone to light with a judgment clout,
After the feast of tear-stuffed time and thistles
In a room with a stuffed fox and a stale fern,
I stand, for this memorial's sake, alone
In the snivelling hours with dead, humped Ann
Whose hooded, fountain heart once fell in puddles
Round the parched worlds of Wales and drowned each sun
(Though this for her is a monstrous image blindly
Magnified out of praise; her death was a still drop;
She would not have me sinking in the holy
Flood of her heart's fame; she would lie dumb and deep
And need no druid of her broken body).
But I, Ann's bard on a raised hearth, call all
The seas to service that her wood-tongued virtue
Babble like a bellbuoy over the hymning heads,
Bow down the walls of the ferned and foxy woods
That her love sing and swing through a brown chapel,
Bless her bent spirit with four, crossing birds.
Her flesh was meek as milk, but this skyward statue
With the wild breast and blessed and giant skull

9

Is carved from her in a room with a wet window
In a fiercely mourning house in a crooked year.
I know her scrubbed and sour humble hands
Lie with religion in their cramp, her threadbare
Whisper in a damp word, her wits drilled hollow,
Her fist of a face died clenched on a round pain;
And sculptured Ann is seventy years of stone.
These cloud-sopped, marble hands, this monumental
Argument of the hewn voice, gesture and psalm,
Storm me forever over her grave until
The stuffed lung of the fox twitch and cry Love
And the strutting fern lay seeds on the black sill.

Once it was the colour of saying

Once it was the colour of saying
Soaked my table the uglier side of a hill
With a capsized field where a school sat still
And a black and white patch of girls grew playing;
The gentle seaslides of saying I must undo
That all the charmingly drowned arise to cockcrow and
    kill.
When I whistled with mitching boys through a reservoir
    park
Where at night we stoned the cold and cuckoo
Lovers in the dirt of their leafy beds,
The shade of their trees was a word of many shades
And a lamp of lightning for the poor in the dark;
Now my saying shall be my undoing,
And every stone I wind off like a reel.

A Refusal to Mourn the Death, by Fire, of a Child in London

Never until the mankind making
Bird beast and flower
Fathering and all humbling darkness
Tells with silence the last light breaking
And the still hour
Is come of the sea tumbling in harness

And I must enter again the round
Zion of the water bead
And the synagogue of the ear of corn
Shall I let pray the shadow of a sound
Or sow my salt seed
In the least valley of sackcloth to mourn

The majesty and burning of the child's death.
I shall not murder
The mankind of her going with a grave truth
Nor blaspheme down the stations of the breath
With any further
Elegy of innocence and youth.

Deep with the first dead lies London's daughter,
Robed in the long friends,
The grains beyond age, the dark veins of her mother,
Secret by the unmourning water
Of the riding Thames.
After the first death, there is no other.

Deaths and Entrances

On almost the incendiary eve
  Of several near deaths,
When one at the great least of your best loved
  And always known must leave
Lions and fires of his flying breath,
  Of your immortal friends
Who'd raise the organs of the counted dust
  To shoot and sing your praise,
One who called deepest down shall hold his peace
  That cannot sink or cease
  Endlessly to his wound
In many married London's estranging grief.

On almost the incendiary eve
  When at your lips and keys,
Locking, unlocking, the murdered strangers weave,
  One who is most unknown,
Your polestar neighbour, sun of another street,
  Will dive up to his tears.
He'll bathe his raining blood in the male sea
  Who strode for your own dead
And wind his globe out of your water thread
  And load the throats of shells
  With every cry since light
Flashed first across his thunderclapping eyes.

On almost the incendiary eve
  Of deaths and entrances,
When near and strange wounded on London's waves
  Have sought your single grave,

One enemy, of many, who knows well
　　Your heart is luminous
In the watched dark, quivering through locks and caves,
　　Will pull the thunderbolts
To shut the sun, plunge, mount your darkened keys
　　And sear just riders back,
　　Until that one loved least
Looms the last Samson of your zodiac.

In my Craft or Sullen Art

In my craft or sullen art
Exercised in the still night
When only the moon rages
And the lovers lie abed
With all their griefs in their arms,
I labour by singing light
Not for ambition or bread
Or the strut and trade of charms
On the ivory stages
But for the common wages
Of their most secret heart.

Not for the proud man apart
From the raging moon I write
On these spindrift pages
Nor for the towering dead
With their nightingales and psalms
But for the lovers, their arms
Round the griefs of the ages,
Who pay no praise or wages
Nor heed my craft or art.

Ceremony After a Fire Raid

Myselves
The grievers
Grieve
Among the street burned to tireless death
A child of a few hours
With its kneading mouth
Charred on the black breast of the grave
The mother dug, and its arms full of fires.

Begin
With singing
Sing
Darkness kindled back into beginning
When the caught tongue nodded blind,
A star was broken
Into the centuries of the child
Myselves grieve now, and miracles cannot atone.

Forgive
Us forgive
Us your death that myselves the believers
May hold it in a great flood
Till the blood shall spurt,
And the dust shall sing like a bird
As the grains blow, as your death grows, through our heart.
Crying
Your dying
Cry,

Child beyond cockcrow, by the fire-dwarfed
Street we chant the flying sea
In the body bereft.
Love is the last light spoken. Oh
Seed of sons in the loin of the black husk left.

II

I know not whether
Adam or Eve, the adorned holy bullock
Or the white ewe lamb
Or the chosen virgin
Laid in her snow
On the altar of London,
Was the first to die
In the cinder of the little skull,
O bride and bride groom
O Adam and Eve together
Lying in the lull
Under the sad breast of the head stone
White as the skeleton
Of the garden of Eden.

I know the legend
Of Adam and Eve is never for a second
Silent in my service
Over the dead infants
Over the one
Child who was priest and servants,
Word, singers, and tongue
In the cinder of the little skull,
Who was the serpent's
Night fall and the fruit like a sun,

Man and woman undone,
Beginning crumbled back to darkness
Bare as the nurseries
Of the garden of wilderness.

III

Into the organpipes and steeples
Of the luminous cathedrals,
Into the weathercocks' molten mouths
Rippling in twelve-winded circles,
Into the dead clock burning the hour
Over the urn of sabbaths
Over the whirling ditch of daybreak
Over the sun's hovel and the slum of fire
And the golden pavements laid in requiems,
Into the bread in a wheatfield of flames,
Into the wine burning like brandy,
The masses of the sea
The masses of the sea under
The masses of the infant-bearing sea
Erupt, fountain, and enter to utter for ever
Glory glory glory
The sundering ultimate kingdom of genesis' thunder.

Ballad of the Long-legged Bait

The bows glided down, and the coast
Blackened with birds took a last look
At his thrashing hair and whale-blue eye;
The trodden town rang its cobbles for luck.

Then goodbye to the fishermanned
Boat with its anchor free and fast
As a bird hooking over the sea,
High and dry by the top of the mast,

Whispered the affectionate sand
And the bulwarks of the dazzled quay.
For my sake sail, and never look back,
Said the looking land.

Sails drank the wind, and white as milk
He sped into the drinking dark;
The sun shipwrecked west on a pearl
And the moon swam out of its hulk.

Funnels and masts went by in a whirl.
Goodbye to the man on the sea-legged deck
To the gold gut that sings on his reel
To the bait that stalked out of the sack,

For we saw him throw to the swift flood
A girl alive with his hooks through her lips;
All the fishes were rayed in blood,
Said the dwindling ships.

Goodbye to chimneys and funnels,
Old wives that spin in the smoke,
He was blind to the eyes of candles
In the praying windows of waves

But heard his bait buck in the wake
And tussle in a shoal of loves.
Now cast down your rod, for the whole
Of the sea is hilly with whales,

She longs among horses and angels,
The rainbow-fish bend in her joys,
Floated the lost cathedral
Chimes of the rocked buoys.

Where the anchor rode like a gull
Miles over the moonstruck boat
A squall of birds bellowed and fell,
A cloud blew the rain from its throat;

He saw the storm smoke out to kill
With fuming bows and ram of ice,
Fire on starlight, rake Jesu's stream;
And nothing shone on the water's face

But the oil and bubble of the moon,
Plunging and piercing in his course
The lured fish under the foam
Witnessed with a kiss.

Whales in the wake like capes and Alps
Quaked the sick sea and snouted deep,
Deep the great bushed bait with raining lips
Slipped the fins of those humpbacked tons

And fled their love in a weaving dip.
Oh, Jericho was falling in their lungs!
She nipped and dived in the nick of love,
Spun on a spout like a long-legged ball

Till every beast blared down in a swerve
Till every turtle crushed from his shell
Till every bone in the rushing grave
Rose and crowed and fell!

Good luck to the hand on the rod,
There is thunder under its thumbs;
Gold gut is a lightning thread,
His fiery reel sings off its flames,

The whirled boat in the burn of his blood
Is crying from nets to knives,
Oh the shearwater birds and their boatsized brood
Oh the bulls of Biscay and their calves

Are making under the green, laid veil
The long-legged beautiful bait their wives.
Break the black news and paint on a sail
Huge weddings in the waves,

Over the wakeward-flashing spray
Over the gardens of the floor
Clash out the mounting dolphin's day,
My mast is a bell-spire,

Strike and smoothe, for my decks are drums,
Sing through the water-spoken prow
The octopus walking into her limbs
The polar eagle with his tread of snow.

From salt-lipped beak to the kick of the stern
Sing how the sea has kissed her dead!
The long, laid minute's bride drifts on
Old in her cruel bed.

Over the graveyard in the water
Mountains and galleries beneath
Nightingale and hyena
Rejoicing for the drafting death

Sing and howl through sand and anemone
Valley and sahara in a shell,
Oh all the wanting flesh his enemy
Thrown to the sea in the shell of a girl

Is old as water and plain as an eel;
Always goodbye to the long-legged bread
Scattered in the paths of his heels
For the salty birds fluttered and fed

And the tall grains foamed in their bills;
Always goodbye to the fires of the face,
For the crab-backed dead on the sea-bed rose
And scuttled over her eyes,

The blind, clawed stare is cold as sleet.
The tempter under the eyelid
Who shows to the selves asleep
Mast-high moon-white women naked

Walking in wishes and lovely for shame
Is dumb and gone with his flame of brides.
Sussanah's drowned in the bearded stream
And no one stirs at Sheba's side

But the hungry kings of the tides;
Sin who had a woman's shape
Sleeps till Silence blows on a cloud
And all the lifted waters walk and leap.

Lucifer that bird's dropping
Out of the sides of the north
Has melted away and is lost
Is always lost in her vaulted breath,

Venus lies star-struck in her wound
And the sensual ruins make
Seasons over the liquid world,
White springs in the dark.

Always goodbye, cried the voices through the shell,
Goodbye always for the flesh is cast
And the fisherman winds his reel
With no more desire than a ghost.

Always good luck, praised the finned in the feather
Bird after dark and the laughing fish
As the sails drank up the hail of thunder
And the long-tailed lightning lit his catch.

The boat swims into the six-year weather,
A wind throws a shadow and it freezes fast.
See what the gold gut drags from under
Mountains and galleries to the crest!

See what clings to hair and skull
As the boat skims on with drinking wings!
The statues of great rain stand still,
And the flakes fall like hills.

Sing and strike his heavy haul
Toppling up the boatside in a snow of light!
His decks are drenched with miracles.
Oh miracle of fishes! The long dead bite!

Out of the urn the size of a man
Out of the room the weight of his trouble
Out of the house that holds a town
In the continent of a fossil

One by one in dust and shawl,
Dry as echoes and insect-faced,
His fathers cling to the hand of the girl
And the dead hand leads the past,

Leads them as children and as air
On to the blindly tossing tops;
The centuries throw back their hair
And the old men sing from newborn lips:

Time is bearing another son.
Kill Time! She turns in her pain!
The oak is felled in the acorn
And the hawk in the egg kills the wren.

He who blew the great fire in
And died on a hiss of flames
Or walked on the earth in the evening
Counting the denials of the grains

Clings to her drifting hair, and climbs;
And he who taught their lips to sing
Weeps like the risen sun among
The liquid choirs of his tribes.

The rod bends low, divining land,
And through the sundered water crawls
A garden holding to her hand
With birds and animals

With men and women and waterfalls
Trees cool and dry in the whirlpool of ships
And stunned and still on the green, laid veil
Sand with legends in its virgin laps

And prophets loud on the burned dunes;
Insects and valleys hold her thighs hard,
Time and places grip her breast bone,
She is breaking with seasons and clouds;

Round her trailed wrist fresh water weaves,
With moving fish and rounded stones
Up and down the greater waves
A separate river breathes and runs;

Strike and sing his catch of fields
For the surge is sown with barley,
The cattle graze on the covered foam,
The hills have footed the waves away,

With wild sea fillies and soaking bridles
With salty colts and gales in their limbs
All the horses of his haul of miracles
Gallop through the arched, green farms,

Trot and gallop with gulls upon them
And thunderbolts in their manes.
O Rome and Sodom Tomorrow and London
The country tide is cobbled with towns,

And steeples pierce the cloud on her shoulder
And the streets that the fisherman combed
When his long-legged flesh was a wind on fire
And his loin was a hunting flame

Coil from the thoroughfares of her hair
And terribly lead him home alive
Lead her prodigal home to his terror,
The furious ox-killing house of love.

Down, down, down, under the ground,
Under the floating villages,
Turns the moon-chained and water-wound
Metropolis of fishes,

There is nothing left of the sea but its sound,
Under the earth the loud sea walks,
In deathbeds of orchards the boat lies down
And the bait is drowned among hayricks,

Land, land, land, nothing remains
Of the pacing, famous sea but its speech,
And into its talkative seven tombs
The anchor dives through the floors of a church.

Goodbye, good luck, struck the sun and the moon,
To the fisherman lost on the land.
He stands alone at the door of his home,
With his long-legged heart in his hand.

Fern Hill

Now as I was young and easy under the apple boughs
About the lilting house and happy as the grass was green,
    The night above the dingle starry,
      Time let me hail and climb
    Golden in the heydays of his eyes,
And honoured among wagons I was prince of the apple
          towns
And once below a time I lordly had the trees and leaves
      Trail with daisies and barley
    Down the rivers of the windfall light.

And as I was green and carefree, famous among the
          barns
About the happy yard and singing as the farm was home,
    In the sun that is young once only,
      Time let me play and be
    Golden in the mercy of his means,
And green and golden I was huntsman and herdsman, the
          calves
Sang to my horn, the foxes on the hills barked clear and
          cold,
      And the sabbath rang slowly
    In the pebbles of the holy streams.

All the sun long it was running, it was lovely, the hay
Fields high as the house, the tunes from the chimneys, it
          was air
    And playing, lovely and watery
      And fire green as grass.
    And nightly under the simple stars

As I rode to sleep the owls were bearing the farm away,
All the moon long I heard, blessed among stables, the
night-jars
Flying with the ricks, and the horses
Flashing into the dark.

And then to awake, and the farm, like a wanderer white
With the dew, come back, the cock on his shoulder: it
was all
Shining, it was Adam and maiden,
The sky gathered again
And the sun grew round that very day.
So it must have been after the birth of the simple light
In the first, spinning place, the spellbound horses walking
warm
Out of the whinnying green stable
On to the fields of praise.

And honoured among foxes and pheasants by the gay
house
Under the new made clouds and happy as the heart was
long,
In the sun born over and over,
I ran my heedless ways,
My wishes raced through the house high hay
And nothing I cared, at my sky blue trades, that time allows
In all his tuneful turning so few and such morning songs
Before the children green and golden
Follow him out of grace,

Nothing I cared, in the lamb white days, that time would
take me
Up to the swallow thronged loft by the shadow of my
hand,

In the moon that is always rising,
   Nor that riding to sleep
I should hear him fly with the high fields
And wake to the farm forever fled from the childless land.
Oh as I was young and easy in the mercy of his means,
   Time held me green and dying
Though I sang in my chains like the sea.

Over Sir John's hill

Over Sir John's hill,
The hawk on fire hangs still;
In a hoisted cloud, at drop of dusk, he pulls to his claws
And gallows, up the rays of his eyes the small birds of
    the bay
And the shrill child's play
Wars
Of the sparrows and such who swansing, dusk, in wrang-
    ling hedges.
And blithely they squawk
To fiery tyburn over the wrestle of elms until
The flash the noosed hawk
Crashes, and slowly the fishing holy stalking heron
In the river Towy below bows his tilted headstone.

Flash, and the plumes crack,
And a black cap of jack-
Daws Sir John's just hill dons, and again the gulled birds
    hare
To the hawk on fire, the halter height, over Towy's fins,
In a whack of wind.
There
Where the elegiac fisherbird stabs and paddles
In the pebbly dab-filled
Shallow and sedge, and 'dilly dilly,' calls the loft hawk,
'Come and be killed,'
I open the leaves of the water at a passage
Of psalms and shadows among the pincered sandcrabs
    prancing
And read, in a shell,

Death clear as a buoy's bell:
All praise of the hawk on fire in hawk-eyed dusk be sung,
When his viperish fuse hangs looped with flames under the brand
Wing, and blest shall
Young
Green chickens of the bay and bushes cluck, 'dilly dilly,
Come let us die.'
We grieve as the blithe birds, never again, leave shingle and elm,
The heron and I,
I young Aesop fabling to the near night by the dingle
Of eels, saint heron hymning in the shell-hung distant

Crystal harbour vale
Where the sea cobbles sail,
And wharves of water where the walls dance and the white cranes stilt.
It is the heron and I, under judging Sir John's elmed
Hill, tell-tale the knelled
Guilt
Of the led-astray birds whom God, for their breast of whistles,
Have mercy on,
God in his whirlwind silence save, who marks the sparrows hail,
For their souls' song.
Now the heron grieves in the weeded verge. Through windows
Of dusk and water I see the tilting whispering

Heron, mirrored, go,
As the snapt feathers snow,
Fishing in the tear of the Towy. Only a hoot owl

Hollows, a grassblade blown in cupped hands, in the
    looted elms
And no green cocks or hens
Shout
Now on Sir John's hill. The heron, ankling the scaly
Lowlands of the waves,
Makes all the music; and I who hear the tune of the slow,
Wear-willow river, grave,
Before the lunge of the night, the notes on this time-
    shaken
Stone for the sake of the souls of the slain birds sailing.

Poem on his birthday

In the mustardseed sun,
By full tilt river and switchback sea
    Where the cormorants scud,
In his house on stilts high among beaks
    And palavers of birds
This sandgrain day in the bent bay's grave
    He celebrates and spurns
His driftwood thirty-fifth wind turned age;
    Herons spire and spear.

Under and round him go
Flounders, gulls, on their cold, dying trails,
    Doing what they are told,
Curlews aloud in the congered waves
    Work at their ways to death,
And the rhymer in the long tongued room,
    Who tolls his birthday bell,
Toils towards the ambush of his wounds;
    Herons, steeple stemmed, bless.

In the thistledown fall,
He sings towards anguish; finches fly
    In the claw tracks of hawks
On a seizing sky; small fishes glide
    Through wynds and shells of drowned
Ship towns to pastures of otters. He
    In his slant, racking house
And the hewn coils of his trade perceives
    Herons walk in their shroud,

33

The livelong river's robe
Of minnows wreathing around their prayer;
    And far at sea he knows,
Who slaves to his crouched, eternal end
    Under a serpent cloud,
Dolphins dive in their turnturtle dust,
    The rippled seals streak down
To kill and their own tide daubing blood
    Slides good in the sleek mouth.

    In a cavernous, swung
Wave's silence, wept white angelus knells.
    Thirty-five bells sing struck
On skull and scar where his loves lie wrecked,
    Steered by the falling stars.
And tomorrow weeps in a blind cage
    Terror will rage apart
Before chains break to a hammer flame
    And love unbolts the dark

    And freely he goes lost
In the unknown, famous light of great
    And fabulous, dear God.
Dark is a way and light is a place,
    Heaven that never was
Nor will be ever is always true,
    And, in that brambled void,
Plenty as blackberries in the woods
    The dead grow for His joy.

    There he might wander bare
With the spirits of the horseshoe bay
    Or the stars' seashore dead,
Marrow of eagles, the roots of whales

And wishbones of wild geese,
With blessed, unborn God and His Ghost,
  And every soul His priest,
Gulled and chanter in young Heaven's fold
  Be at cloud quaking peace,

  But dark is a long way,
He, on the earth of the night, alone
  With all the living, prays,
Who knows the rocketing wind will blow
  The bones out of the hills,
And the scythed boulders bleed, and the last
  Rage shattered waters kick
Masts and fishes to the still quick stars,
  Faithlessly unto Him

  Who is the light of old
And air shaped Heaven where souls grow wild
  As horses in the foam:
Oh, let me midlife mourn by the shrined
  And druid herons' vows
The voyage to ruin I must run,
  Dawn ships clouted aground,
Yet, though I cry with tumbledown tongue,
  Count my blessings aloud:

  Four elements and five
Senses, and man a spirit in love
  Tangling through this spun slime
To his nimbus bell cool kingdom come
  And the lost, moonshine domes,
And the sea that hides his secret selves
  Deep in its black, base bones,
Lulling of spheres in the seashell flesh,
  And this last blessing most,

That the closer I move
To death, one man through his sundered hulks,
   The louder the sun blooms
And the tusked, ramshackling sea exults;
   And every wave of the way
And gale I tackle, the whole world then,
   With more triumphant faith
Than ever was since the world was said,
   Spins its morning of praise,

   I hear the bouncing hills
Grow larked and greener at berry brown
   Fall and the dew larks sing
Taller this thunderclap spring, and how
   More spanned with angels ride
The mansouled fiery islands! Oh,
   Holier then their eyes,
And my shining men no more alone
   As I sail out to die.

Part II

STORIES

A VISIT TO GRANDPA'S

IN THE middle of the night I woke from a dream full of whips and lariats as long as serpents, and runaway coaches on mountain passes, and wide, windy gallops over cactus fields, and I heard the man in the next room crying, 'Gee-up!' and 'Whoa!' and trotting his tongue on the roof of his mouth.

It was the first time I had stayed in grandpa's house. The floorboards had squeaked like mice as I climbed into bed, and the mice between the walls had creaked like wood as though another visitor was walking on them. It was a mild summer night, but curtains had flapped and branches beaten against the window. I had pulled the sheets over my head, and soon was roaring and riding in a book.

'Whoa there, my beauties!' cried grandpa. His voice sounded very young and loud, and his tongue had powerful hooves, and he made his bedroom into a great meadow. I thought I would see if he was ill, or had set his bedclothes on fire, for my mother had said that he lit his pipe under the blankets, and had warned me to run to his help if I smelt smoke in the night. I went on tiptoe through the darkness to his bedroom door, brushing against the furniture and upsetting a candlestick with a thump. When I saw there was a light in the room I felt frightened, and as I opened the door I heard grandpa shout, 'Gee-up!' as loudly as a bull with a megaphone.

He was sitting straight up in bed and rocking from side to side as though the bed were on a rough road; the knotted edges of the counterpane were his reins; his invisible horse stood in a shadow beyond the bedside candle. Over a white flannel nightshirt he was wearing a red waistcoat with walnut-sized brass buttons. The over-filled bowl of his pipe smouldered among his whiskers like a little, burning hayrick on a stick. At the sight of me, his hands dropped from the reins and lay blue and quiet, the bed stopped still on a level road, he muffled his tongue into silence, and the horses drew softly up.

'Is there anything the matter, grandpa?' I asked, though the clothes were not on fire. His face in the candle-light looked like a ragged quilt pinned upright on the black air and patched all over with goat-beards.

He stared at me mildly. Then he blew down his pipe, scattering the sparks and making a high, wet dog-whistle of the stem, and shouted: 'Ask no questions.'

After a pause, he said slyly: 'Do you ever have night-mares, boy?'

I said: 'No.'

'Oh, yes, you do,' he said.

I said I was woken by a voice that was shouting to horses.

'What did I tell you?' he said. 'You eat too much. Who ever heard of horses in a bedroom?'

He fumbled under his pillow, brought out a small tinkling bag, and carefully untied its strings. He put a sovereign in my hand, and said: 'Buy a cake.' I thanked him and wished him good night.

As I closed my bedroom door, I heard his voice crying loudly and gaily, 'Gee-up! gee-up!' and the rocking of the travelling bed.

In the morning I woke from a dream of fiery horses on a plain that was littered with furniture, and of large, cloudy men who rode six horses at a time and whipped them with burning bed-clothes. Grandpa was at break-fast, dressed in deep black. After breakfast he said, 'There was a terrible loud wind last night,' and sat in his arm-chair by the hearth to make clay balls for the fire. Later in the morning he took me for a walk, through Johns-town village and into the fields on the Llanstephan road.

A man with a whippet said, 'There's a nice morning, Mr Thomas,' and when he had gone, leanly as his dog, into the short-treed green wood he should not have entered because of the notices, grandpa said: 'There, do you hear what he called you? Mister!'

We passed by small cottages, and all the men who leant on the gates congratulated grandpa on the fine morning. We passed through the wood full of pigeons, and their wings broke the branches as they rushed to the tops of the trees. Among the soft, contented voices and the loud, timid flying, grandpa said, like a man calling across a field: 'If you heard those old birds in the night, you'd wake me up and say there were horses in the trees.'

We walked back slowly, for he was tired, and the lean man stalked out of the forbidden wood with a rabbit held as gently over his arm as a girl's arm in a warm sleeve.

On the last day but one of my visit I was taken to Llanstephan in a governess cart, pulled by a short, weak pony. Grandpa might have been driving a bison, so tightly he held the reins, so ferociously cracked the long whip, so blasphemously shouted warnings to boys who played in the road, so stoutly stood with his gaitered legs apart and cursed the demon strength and wilfulness of his tottering pony.

'Look out, boy!' he cried when we came to each corner, and pulled and tugged and jerked and sweated and waved his whip like a rubber sword. And when the pony had crept miserably round each corner, grandpa turned to me with a sighing smile: 'We weathered that one, boy.'

When we came to Llanstephan village at the top of the hill, he left the cart by the 'Edwinsford Arms' and patted the pony's muzzle and gave it sugar, saying: 'You're a weak little pony, Jim, to pull big men like us.'

He had strong beer and I had lemonade, and he paid Mrs Edwinsford with a sovereign out of the tinkling bag; she inquired after his health, and he said that Llangadock was better for the tubes. We went to look at the churchyard and the sea, and sat in the wood called the Sticks, and stood on the concert platform in the middle of the wood where visitors sang on midsummer nights and, year by year, the innocent of the village was elected mayor. Grandpa paused at the churchyard and pointed over the iron gate at the angelic headstones and the poor wooden crosses. 'There's no sense in lying there,' he said.

We journeyed back furiously: Jim was a bison again.

I woke late on my last morning, out of dreams where the Llanstephan sea carried bright sailing boats as long as liners; and heavenly choirs in the Sticks, dressed in bards' robes and brass-buttoned wiastcoats, sang in a strange Welsh to the departing sailors. Grandpa was not at breakfast; he rose early. I walked in the fields with a new sling, and shot at the Towy gulls and the rooks in the parsonage trees. A warm wind blew from the summer points of the weather; a morning mist climbed from the ground and floated among the trees and hid the noisy birds; in the mist and the wind my pebbles flew lightly up like hailstones in a world on its head. The morning passed without a bird falling.

I broke my sling and returned for the midday meal through the parson's orchard. Once, grandpa told me, the parson had bought three ducks at Carmarthen Fair and made a pond for them in the centre of the garden, but they waddled to the gutter under the crumbling doorsteps of the house, and swam and quacked there. When I reached the end of the orchard path, I looked through a hole in the hedge and saw that the parson had made a tunnel through the rockery that was between the gutter and the pond and had set up a notice in plain writing: 'This way to the pond.'

The ducks were still swimming under the steps.

Grandpa was not in the cottage. I went into the garden, but grandpa was not staring at the fruit trees. I called across to a man who leant on a spade in the field beyond the garden hedge: 'Have you seen my grandpa this morning?'

He did not stop digging, and answered over his shoulder: 'I seen him in his fancy waistcoat.'

Griff, the barber, lived in the next cottage. I called to him through the open door: 'Mr Griff, have you seen my grandpa?'

The barber came out in his shirtsleeves.

I said: 'He's wearing his best waistcoat.' I did not know if it was important, but grandpa wore his waistcoat only in the night.

'Has grandpa been to Llanstephan?' asked Mr Griff anxiously.

'He went there yesterday in a little trap,' I said.

He hurried indoors and I heard him talking in Welsh, and he came out again with his white coat on, and he carried a striped and coloured walking-stick. He strode down the village street and I ran by his side.

When we stopped at the tailor's shop, he cried out, 'Dan!' and Dan tailor stepped from his window where he sat like an Indian priest but wearing a derby hat. 'Dai Thomas has got his waistcoat on,' said Mr Griff, 'and he's been to Llanstephan.'

As Dan tailor searched for his overcoat, Mr Griff was

striding on. 'Will Evans,' he called outside the carpenter's shop, 'Dai Thomas has been to Llanstephan, and he's got his waistcoat on.'

'I'll tell Morgan now,' said the carpenter's wife out of the hammering, sawing darkness of the shop.

We called at the butcher's shop and Mr Price's house, and Mr Griff repeated his message like a town crier.

We gathered together in Johnstown square. Dan tailor had his bicycle, Mr Price his pony trap. Mr Griff, the butcher, Morgan carpenter, and I climbed into the shaking trap, and we trotted off towards Carmarthen town. The tailor led the way, ringing his bell as though there were a fire or a robbery, and an old woman by the gate of a cottage at the end of the street ran inside like a pelted hen. Another woman waved a bright handkerchief.

'Where are we going?' I asked.

Grandpa's neighbours were as solemn as old men with black hats and jackets on the outskirts of a fair. Mr Griff shook his head and mourned: 'I didn't expect this again from Dai Thomas.'

'Not after last time,' said Mr Price sadly.

We trotted on, we crept up Constitution Hill, we rattled down into Lammas Street, and the tailor still rang his bell and a dog ran, squealing, in front of his wheels. As we clip-clopped over the cobbles that led down to the Towy bridge, I remembered grandpa's nightly noisy journeys that rocked the bed and shook the walls, and I saw his gay waistcoat in a vision and his patchwork head tufted and smiling in the candlelight. The tailor before us turned round on his saddle, his bicycle wobbled and skidded. 'I see Dai Thomas!' he cried.

The trap rattled on to the bridge, and I saw grandpa there: the buttons of his waistcoat shone in the sun, he wore his tight, black Sunday trousers and a tall, dusty hat

I had seen in a cupboard in the attic, and he carried an ancient bag. He bowed to us. 'Good morning, Mr Price,' he said, 'and Mr Griff and Mr Morgan and Mr Evans.' To me he said: 'Good morning, boy.'

Mr Griff pointed his coloured stick at him.

'And what do you think you are doing on Carmarthen bridge in the middle of the afternoon', he said sternly, 'with your best waistcoat and your old hat?'

Grandpa did not answer, but inclined his face to the river wind, so that his beard was set dancing and wagging as though he talked, and watched the coracle men move, like turtles, on the shore.

Mr Griff raised his stunted barber's pole. 'And where do you think you are going', he said, 'with your old black bag?'

Grandpa said: 'I am going to Llangadock to be buried.' And he watched the coracle shells slip into the water lightly, and the gulls complain over the fish-filled water as bitterly as Mr Price complained:

'But you aren't dead yet, Dai Thomas.'

For a moment grandpa reflected, then: 'There's no sense in lying dead in Llanstephan,' he said. 'The ground is comfy in Llangadock; you can twitch your legs without putting them in the sea.'

His neighbours moved close to him. They said: 'You aren't dead, Mr Thomas.'

'How can you be buried, then?'

'Nobody's going to bury you in Llanstephan.'

'Come on home, Mr Thomas.'

'There's strong beer for tea.'

'And cake.'

But grandpa stood firmly on the bridge, and clutched his bag to his side, and stared at the flowing river and the sky, like a prophet who has no doubt.

EXTRAORDINARY LITTLE
COUGH

ONE afternoon, in a particularly bright and glowing August, some years before I knew I was happy, George Hooping, whom we called Little Cough, Sidney Evans, Dan Davies, and I sat on the roof of a lorry travelling to the end of the Peninsula. It was a tall, six-wheeled lorry, from which we could spit on the roofs of the passing cars and throw our apple stumps at women on the pavement. One stump caught a man on a bicycle in the middle of the back, he swerved across the road, for a moment we sat quiet and George Hooping's face grew pale. And if the lorry runs over him, I thought calmly as the man on the bicycle swayed towards the hedge, he'll get killed and I'll be sick on my trousers and perhaps on Sidney's too, and we'll be arrested and hanged, except George Hooping who didn't have an apple.

But the lorry swept past; behind us, the bicycle drove into the hedge, the man stood up and waved his fist, and I waved my cap back at him.

'You shouldn't have waved your cap,' said Sidney Evans, 'he'll know what school we're in.' He was clever, dark, and careful, and had a purse and a wallet.

'We're not in school now.'

'Nobody can expel me,' said Dan Davies. He was leaving next term to serve in his father's fruit shop for a salary.

We all wore haversacks, except George Hooping whose mother had given him a brown-paper parcel that kept coming undone, and carried a suitcase each. I had placed

46

a coat over my suitcase because the initials on it were 'N. T.' and everybody would know that it belonged to my sister. Inside the lorry were two tents, a box of food, a packing-case of kettles and saucepans and knives and forks, an oil lamp, a primus stove, ground sheets and blankets, a gramophone with three records, and a table-cloth from George Hooping's mother.

We were going to camp for a fortnight in Rhossilli, in a field above the sweeping five-mile beach. Sidney and Dan had stayed there last year, coming back brown and swearing, full of stories of campers' dances round the fires at midnight, and elderly girls from the training college who sun-bathed naked on ledges of rocks surrounded by laughing boys, and singing in bed that lasted until dawn. But George had never left home for more than a night; and then, he told me one half-holiday when it was raining and there was nothing to do but stay in the wash-house racing his guinea-pigs giddily along the benches, it was only to stay in St Thomas, three miles from his house, with an aunt who could see through the walls and who knew what a Mrs Hoskin was doing in the kitchen.

'How much further?' asked George Hooping, clinging to his split parcel, trying in secret to push back socks and suspenders, enviously watching the solid green fields skim by as though the roof were a raft on an ocean with a motor in it. Anything upset his stomach, even liquorice and sherbet, but I alone knew that he wore long combinations in the summer with his name stitched in red on them.

'Miles and miles,' Dan said.

'Thousands of miles,' I said. 'It's Rhossilli, U.S.A. We're going to camp on a bit of rock that wobbles in the wind.'

'And we have to tie the rock on to a tree.'

'Cough can use his suspenders,' Sidney said.

The lorry roared round a corner—'Upsy-daisy! Did you feel it then, Cough? It was on one wheel'—and below us, beyond fields and farms, the sea, with a steamer puffing on its far edge, shimmered.

'Do you see the sea down there, it's shimmering, Dan,' I said.

George Hooping pretended to forget the lurch of the slippery roof and, from that height, the frightening smallness of the sea. Gripping the rail of the roof, he said: 'My father saw a killer whale.' The conviction in his voice died quickly as he began. He beat against the wind with his cracked, treble voice, trying to make us believe. I knew he wanted to find a boast so big it would make our hair stand up and stop the wild lorry.

'Your father's a herbalist.' But the smoke on the horizon was the white, curling fountain the whale blew through his nose, and its black nose was the bow of the poking ship.

'Where did he keep it, Cough, in the wash-house?'

'He saw it in Madagascar. It had tusks as long as from here to, from here to . . .'

'From here to Madagascar.'

All at once the threat of a steep hill disturbed him. No longer bothered about the adventures of his father, a small, dusty, skull-capped and alpaca-coated man standing and mumbling all day in a shop full of herbs and curtained holes in the wall, where old men with backache and young girls in trouble waited for consultations in the half-dark, he stared at the hill swooping up and clung to Dan and me.

'She's doing fifty!'

'The brakes have gone, Cough!'

He twisted away from us, caught hard with both hands on the rail, pulled and trembled, pressed on a case behind him with his foot, and steered the lorry to safety round a stone-walled corner and up a gentler hill to a gate of a battered farmhouse.

Leading down from the gate, there was a lane to the first beach. It was high tide, and we heard the sea dashing. Four boys on a roof—one tall, dark, regular-featured, precise of speech, in a good suit, a boy of the world; one squat, ungainly, red-haired, his red wrists fighting out of short, frayed sleeves; one heavily spectacled, small-paunched, with indoor shoulders and feet in always unlaced boots wanting to go different ways; one small, thin, indecisively active, quick to get dirty, curly—saw their field in front of them, a fortnight's new home that had thick, pricking hedges for walls, the sea for a front garden, a green gutter for a lavatory, and a wind-struck tree in the very middle.

I helped Dan unload the lorry while Sidney tipped the driver and George struggled with the farmyard gate and looked at the ducks inside. The lorry drove away.

'Let's build our tents by the tree in the middle,' said George.

'Pitch!' Sidney said, unlatching the gate for him.

We pitched our tents in a corner, out of the wind.

'One of us must light the primus,' Sidney said, and, after George had burned his hand, we sat in a circle outside the sleeping-tent talking about motor-cars, content to be in the country, lazily easy in each other's company, thinking to ourselves as we talked, knowing always that the sea dashed on the rocks not far below us and rolled out into the world, and that tomorrow we would bathe and throw a ball on the sands and stone a bottle on a rock and perhaps meet three girls. The oldest would be for

Sidney, the plainest for Dan, and the youngest for me. George broke his spectacles when he spoke to girls; he had to walk off, blind as a bat, and the next morning he would say, 'I'm sorry I had to leave you, but I remembered a message.'

It was past five o'clock. My father and mother would have finished tea; the plates with famous castles on them were cleared from the table; father with a newspaper, mother with socks, were far away in the blue haze to the left, up a hill, in a villa, hearing from the park the faint cries of children drift over the public tennis court, and wondering where I was and what I was doing. I was alone with my friends in a field, with a blade of grass in my mouth saying 'Dempsey would hit him cold', and thinking of the great whale that George's father never saw thrashing on the top of the sea, or plunging underneath, like a mountain.

'Bet you I can beat you to the end of the field.'

Dan and I raced among the cowpads, George thumping at our heels.

'Let's go down to the beach.'

Sidney led the way, running straight as a soldier in his khaki shorts, over a stile, down fields to another, into a wooded valley, up through heather on to a clearing near the edge of the cliff, where two broad boys were wrestling outside a tent. I saw one bite the other in the leg, they both struck expertly and savagely at the face, one struggled clear, and, with a leap, the other had him face to the ground. They were Brazell and Skully.

'Hallo, Brazell and Skully!' said Dan.

Skully had Brazell's arm in a policeman's grip; he gave it two quick twists and stood up, smiling.

'Hallo, boys! Hallo, Little Cough! How's your father?'

'He's very well, thank you.'

Brazell, on the grass, felt for broken bones. 'Hallo, boys! How are your fathers?'

They were the worst and biggest boys in school. Every day for a term they caught me before class began and wedged me in the waste-paper basket and then put the basket on the master's desk. Sometimes I could get out and sometimes not. Brazell was lean, Skully was fat.

'We're camping in Button's field,' said Sidney.

'We're taking a rest cure here,' said Brazell. 'And how is Little Cough these days? Father given him a pill?'

We wanted to run down to the beach, Dan and Sidney and George and I, to be alone together, to walk and shout by the sea in the country, throw stones at the waves, remember adventures and make more to remember.

'We'll come down to the beach with you,' said Skully.

He linked arms with Brazell, and they strolled behind us, imitating George's wayward walk and slashing the grass with switches.

Dan said hopefully: 'Are you camping here for long, Brazell and Skully?'

'For a whole nice fortnight, Davies and Thomas and Evans and Hooping.'

When we reached Mewslade beach and flung ourselves down, as I scooped up sand and it trickled, grain by grain through my fingers, as George peered at the sea through his double lenses and Sidney and Dan heaped sand over his legs, Brazell and Skully sat behind us like two warders.

'We thought of going to Nice for a fortnight,' said Brazell—he rhymed it with ice, dug Skully in the ribs— 'but the air's nicer here for the complexion.'

'It's as good as a herb,' said Skully.

They shared an enormous joke, cuffing and biting and wrestling again, scattering sand in the eyes, until they fell back with laughter, and Brazell wiped the blood from his nose with a piece of picnic paper. George lay covered to the waist in sand. I watched the sea slipping out, with birds quarrelling over it, and the sun beginning to go down patiently.

'Look at Little Cough,' said Brazell. 'Isn't he extraordinary? He's growing out of the sand. Little Cough hasn't got any legs.'

'Poor Little Cough,' said Skully, 'he's the most extraordinary boy in the world.'

'Extraordinary Little Cough,' they said together, 'extraordinary, extraordinary, extraordinary.' They made a song out of it, and both conducted with their switches.

'He can't swim.'

'He can't run.'

'He can't learn.'

'He can't bowl.'

'He can't bat.'

'And I bet he can't make water.'

George kicked the sand from his legs. 'Yes, I can!'

'Can you swim?'

'Can you run?'

'Can you bowl?'

'Leave him alone,' Dan said.

They shuffled nearer to us. The sea was racing out now. Brazell said in a serious voice, wagging his finger: 'Now, quite truthfully, Cough, aren't you extraordinary? Very extraordinary? Say "Yes" or "No".'

'Categorically, "Yes" or "No",' said Skully.

'No,' George said. 'I can swim and I can run and I can play cricket. I'm not frightened of anybody.'

I said: 'He was second in the form last term.'

'Now isn't that extraordinary? If he can be second he can be first. But no, that's too ordinary. Little Cough must be second.'

'The question is answered,' said Skully. 'Little Cough is extraordinary.' They began to sing again.

'He's a very good runner,' Dan said.

'Well, let him prove it. Skully and I ran the whole length of Rhossili sands this morning, didn't we, Skull?'

'Every inch.'

'Can Little Cough do it?'

'Yes,' said George.

'Do it, then.'

'I don't want to.'

'Extraordinary Little Cough can't run,' they sang, 'can't run, can't run.'

Three girls, all fair, came down the cliff-side arm in arm, dressed in short, white trousers. Their arms and legs and throats were brown as berries; I could see when they laughed that their teeth were very white; they stepped on to the beach, and Brazell and Skully stopped singing. Sidney smoothed his hair back, rose casually, put his hands in his pockets and walked towards the girls, who now stood close together, gold and brown, admiring the sunset with little attention, patting their scarves, turning smiles on each other. He stood in front of them, grinned, and saluted: 'Hallo, Gwyneth! do you remember me?'

'La-di-da!' whispered Dan at my side, and made a mock salute to George still peering at the retreating sea.

'Well, if this isn't a surprise!' said the tallest girl. With little studied movements of her hands, as though she were distributing flowers, she introduced Peggy and Jean.

Fat Peggy, I thought, too jolly for me, with hockey legs and tomboy crop, was the girl for Dan; Sidney's Gwyneth was a distinguished piece and quite sixteen, as immaculate and unapproachable as a girl in Ben Evans's stores; but Jean, shy and curly, with butter-coloured hair, was mine. Dan and I walked slowly to the girls.

I made up two remarks: 'Fair's fair, Sidney, no bigamy abroad,' and 'Sorry we couldn't arrange to have the sea in when you came.'

Jean smiled, wriggling her heel in the sand, and I raised my cap.

'Hallo!'

The cap dropped at her feet.

As I bent down, three lumps of sugar fell from my blazer pocket. 'I've been feeding a horse,' I said, and began to blush guiltily when all the girls laughed.

I could have swept the ground with my cap, kissed my hand gaily, called them señoritas, and made them smile without tolerance. Or I could have stayed at a distance, and this would have been better still, my hair blown in the wind, though there was no wind at all that evening, wrapped in mystery and staring at the sun, too aloof to speak to girls; but I knew that all the time my ears would have been burning, my stomach would have been as hollow and as full of voices as a shell. 'Speak to them quickly, before they go away!' a voice would have said insistently over the dramatic silence, as I stood like Valentino on the edge of the bright, invisible bull-ring of the sands. 'Isn't it lovely here!' I said.

I spoke to Jean alone; and this is love, I thought, as she nodded her head and swung her curls and said: 'It's nicer than Porthcawl.'

Brazell and Skully were two big bullies in a nightmare; I forgot them when Jean and I walked up the cliff, and, looking back to see if they were baiting George again or wrestling together, I saw that George had disappeared around the corner of the rocks and that they were talking at the foot of the cliff with Sidney and the two girls.

'What's your name?'

I told her.

'That's Welsh,' she said.

'You've got a beautiful name.'

'Oh, it's just ordinary.'

'Shall I see you again?'

'If you want to.'

'I want to all right! We can go and bathe in the morning. And we can try to get an eagle's egg. Did you know that there were eagles here?'

'No,' she said. 'Who was that handsome boy on the beach, the tall one with dirty trousers?'

'He's not handsome, that's Brazell. He never washes or combs his hair or anything. He's a bully and he cheats.'

'I think he's handsome.'

We walked into Button's field, and I showed her inside the tents and gave her one of George's apples. 'I'd like a cigarette,' she said.

It was nearly dark when the others came. Brazell and Skully were with Gwyneth, one each side of her holding her arms, Sidney was with Peggy, and Dan walked, whistling, behind with his hands in his pockets.

'There's a pair,' said Brazell, 'they've been here all alone and they aren't even holding hands. You want a pill,' he said to me.

'Build Britain's babies,' said Skully.

'Go on!' Gwyneth said. She pushed him away from her, but she was laughing, and she said nothing when he put his arm around her waist.

'What about a bit of fire?' said Brazell.

Jean clapped her hands like an actress. Although I knew I loved her, I didn't like anything she said or did.

'Who's going to make it?'

'He's the best, I'm sure,' she said, pointing to me.

Dan and I collected sticks, and by the time it was quite dark there was a fire crackling. Inside the sleeping-tent,

Brazell and Jean sat close together; her golden head was on his shoulder; Skully, near them, whispered to Gwyneth; Sidney unhappily held Peggy's hand.

'Did you ever see such a sloppy lot?' I said, watching Jean smile in the fiery dark.

'Kiss me, Charley!' said Dan.

We sat by the fire in the corner of the field. The sea, far out, was still making a noise. We heard a few nightbirds. '"Tu-whit! tu-whoo!" Listen! I don't like owls,' Dan said, 'they scratch your eyes out!'—and tried not to listen to the soft voices in the tent. Gwyneth's laughter floated out over the suddenly moonlit field, but Jean, with the beast, was smiling and silent in the covered warmth; I knew her little hand was in Brazell's hand.

'Women!' I said.

Dan spat in the fire.

We were old and alone, sitting beyond desire in the middle of the night, when George appeared, like a ghost, in the firelight and stood there trembling until I said: 'Where've you been? You've been gone hours. Why are you trembling like that?'

Brazell and Skully poked their heads out.

'Hallo, Cough my boy! How's your father? What have you been up to tonight?'

George Hooping could hardly stand. I put my hand on his shoulder to steady him, but he pushed it away.

'I've been running on Rhossilli sands! I ran every bit of it! You said I couldn't, and I did! I've been running and running!'

Someone inside the tent had put a record on the gramophone. It was a selection from *No, No, Nanette*.

'You've been running all the time in the dark, Little Cough?'

'And I bet I ran it quicker than you did, too!' George said.

'I bet you did,' said Brazell.

'Do you think we'd run five miles?' said Skully.

Now the tune was 'Tea for Two'.

'Did you ever hear anything so extraordinary? I told you Cough was extraordinary. Little Cough's been running all night.'

'Extraordinary, extraordinary, extraordinary Little Cough,' they said.

Laughing from the shelter of the tent into the darkness, they looked like a boy with two heads. And when I stared round at George again he was lying on his back fast sleep in the deep grass and his hair was touching the flames.

WHERE TAWE FLOWS

Mr Humphries, Mr Roberts, and young Mr Thomas knocked on the front door of Mr Emlyn Evans's small villa, 'Lavengro', punctually at nine o'clock in the evening. They waited, hidden behind a veronica bush, while Mr Evans shuffled in carpet slippers up the passage from the back room and had trouble with the bolts.

Mr Humphries was a school teacher, a tall, fair man with a stammer, who had written an unsuccessful novel.

Mr Roberts, a cheerful, disreputable man of middle age, was a collector for an insurance company; they called him in the trade a body-snatcher, and he was known among his friends as Burke and Hare, the Welsh Nationalist. He had once held a high position in a brewery office.

Young Mr Thomas was at the moment without employment, but it was understood that he would soon be leaving for London to make a career in Chelsea as a freelance journalist; he was penniless, and hoped, in a vague way, to live on women.

When Mr Evans opened the door and shone his torch down the narrow drive, lighting up the garage and hen-run but missing altogether the whispering bush, the three friends bounded out and cried in threatening voices: 'We're Ogpu men, let us in!'

'We're looking for seditious literature,' said Mr Humphries with difficulty, raising his hand in a salute.

'Heil, Saunders Lewis! and we know where to find it,' said Mr Roberts.

Mr Evans turned off his torch. 'Come in out of the

night, air, boys, and have a drop of something. It's only parsnip wine,' he added.

They removed their hats and coats, piled them on the end of the banister, spoke softly for fear of waking up the twins, George and Celia, and followed Mr Evans into his den.

'Where's the trouble and strife, Mr Evans?' said Mr Roberts in a cockney accent. He warmed his hands in front of the fire and regarded with a smile of surprise, though he visited the house every Friday, the neat rows of books, the ornate roll-top desk that made the parlour into a study, the shining grandfather clock, the photographs of children staring stiffly at a dickybird, the still, delicious home-made wine, that had such an effect, in an old beer bottle, the sleeping tom on the frayed rug. 'At home with the *bourgeoisie.*'

He was himself a homeless bachelor with a past, much in debt, and nothing gave him more pleasure than to envy his friends their wives and comforts and to speak of them intimately and disparagingly.

'In the kitchen,' said Mr Evans, handing out glasses.

'A woman's only place,' said Mr Roberts heartily, 'with one exception.'

Mr Humphries and Mr Thomas arranged the chairs around the fire, and all four sat down, close and confidential and with full glasses in their hands. None of them spoke for a time. They gave one another sly looks, sipped and sighed, lit the cigarettes that Mr Evans produced from a draughts box, and once Mr Humphries glanced at the grandfather clock and winked and put his finger to his lips. Then, as the visitors grew warm and the wine worked and they forgot the bitter night outside, Mr Evans said, with a little shudder of forbidden delight: 'The wife will be going to bed in half an hour. Then we can start the good work. Have you all got yours with you?'

'And the tools,' said Mr Roberts, smacking his side pocket.

'What's the word until then?' said young Mr Thomas. Mr Humphries winked again. 'Mum!'

'I've been waiting for tonight to come round like I used to wait for Saturdays when I was a boy,' said Mr Evans, 'I got a penny then. And it all went on gobstoppers and jelly-babies, too.'

He was a traveller in rubber, rubber toys and syringes and bath mats. Sometimes Mr Roberts called him the poor man's friend to make him blush. 'No! no! no!' he would say, 'you can look at my samples, there's nothing like that there.' He was a Socialist.

'I used to buy a packet of Cinderellas with my penny,' said Mr Roberts, 'and smoke them in the slaughter-house. The sweetest little smoke in the world. You don't see them now.'

'Do you remember old Jim, the caretaker, in the slaughter-house?' asked Mr Evans.

'He was after my time; I'm no chicken, like you boys.'

'You're not old, Mr Roberts, think of G.B.S.'

'No clean Shavianism for me, I'm an unrepentant eater of birds and beasts,' said Mr Roberts.

'Do you eat flowers, too?'

'Oh! oh! you literary men, don't you talk above my head now. I'm only a poor resurrectionist on the knocker.'

'He'd put his hand down in the guts-box and bring you out a rat with its neck broken clean as a match for the price of a glass of beer.'

'And it was beer then.'

'Shop! shop!' Mr Humphries beat on the table with his glass. 'You mustn't waste stories, we'll need them all,' he said. 'Have you got the abattoir anecdote down in your memory book, Mr Thomas?'

'I'll remember it.'

'Don't forget, you can only talk at random now,' said Mr Humphries.

'Okay, Roderick!' Mr Thomas said quickly.

Mr Roberts put his hands over his ears. 'The conversation is getting esoteric,' he said. 'Excuse my French! Mr Evans, have you such a thing as a rook rifle? I want to scare the highbrows off. Did I ever tell you the time I lectured to the John O' London's Society on "The Utility of Uselessness"? That was a poser. I talked about Jack London all the time, and when they said at the end that it wasn't a lecture about what I said it was going to be, I said "Well, it was useless lecturing about that, wasn't it?" and they hadn't a word to say. Mrs Dr Davies was in the front row, you remember her? She gave that first lecture on W. J. Locke and got spoonered in the middle. Remember her talking about the "Bevagged Loveabond," Mr Humphries?'

'Shop! shop!' said Mr Humphries, groaning; 'keep it until after.'

'More parsnip?'

'It goes down the throat like silk, Mr Evans.'

'Like baby's milk.'

'Say when, Mr Roberts.'

'A word of four syllables denoting a period of time. Thank you! I read that on a matchbox.'

'Why don't they have serials on matchboxes? You'd buy the shop up to see what Daphne did next,' Mr Humphries said.

He stopped and looked round in embarrassment at the faces of his friends. Daphne was the name of the grass widow in Manselton for whom Mr Roberts had lost both his reputation and his position in the brewery. He had been in the habit of delivering bottles to her house, free of charge, and he had bought her a cocktail cabinet and given her a hundred pounds and his mother's rings. In return she held large parties and never invited him. Only Mr Thomas had noticed the name, and he was saying: 'No, Mr Humphries, on toilet rolls would be best.'

'When I was in London', Mr Roberts said, 'I stayed with a couple called Armitage in Palmer's Green. He made curtains and blinds. They used to leave each other messages on the toilet paper every single day.'

'If you want to make a Venetian blind', said Mr Evans, 'stick him in the eye with a hatpin.' He felt, always, a little left out of his evenings at home, and he was waiting for Mrs Evans to come in, disapprovingly, from the kitchen.

'I've often had to use, "Dear Tom, don't forget the Watkinses are coming to tea", or, "To Peggy, from Tom, in remembrance". Mr Armitage was a Mosleyite.'

'Thugs,' said Mr Humphries.

'Seriously, what are we going to do about this uniformication of the individual?' Mr Evans asked. Maud was in the kitchen still; he heard her beating the plates.

'Answering your question with another,' said Mr Roberts, putting one hand on Mr Evans's knee, 'what individuality is there left? The mass-age produces the mass-man. The machine produces the robot.'

'As its slave,' Mr Humphries articulated clearly, 'not, mark you, as its master.'

'There you have it. There it is. Tyrannic dominance by a sparking plug, Mr Humphries, and it's flesh and blood that always pays.'

'Any empty glasses?'

Mr Roberts turned his glass upside-down. 'That used to mean, "I'll take on the best man in the room in a bout of fisticuffs", in Llanelly. But seriously, as Mr Evans says, the old-fashioned individualist is a square peg now in a round hole.'

'What a hole!' said Mr Thomas.

'Take our national—what did Onlooker say last week? —our national misleaders.'

'You take them, Mr Roberts, we've got rats already,' Mr Evans said with a nervous laugh. The kitchen was silent. Maud was ready.

'Onlooker is a *nom de plume* for Basil Gorse Williams,' said Mr Humphries. 'Did anyone know that?'

'*Nom de guerre*. Did you see his article on Ramsay Mac? "A sheep in wolf's clothing".'

'Know him!' Mr Roberts said scornfully, 'I've been sick on him.'

Mrs Evans heard the last remark as she came into the room. She was a thin woman with bitter lines, tired hands, the ruins of fine brown eyes, and a superior nose. An unshockable woman, she had once listened to Mr Roberts's description of his haemorrhoids for over an hour on a New Year's Eve and had allowed him, without protest, to call them the grapes of wrath. When sober, Mr Roberts addressed her as 'ma'am' and kept the talk to weather and colds. He sprang to his feet and offered her his chair.

'No, thank you, Mr Roberts,' she said in a clear, hard voice. 'I'm going to bed at once. The cold disagrees with me.'

Go to bed plain Maud, thought young Mr Thomas. 'Will you have a little warm, Mrs Evans, before you retire?' he said.

She shook her head, gave the friends a thin smile, and

said to Mr Evans: 'Put the world right before you come to bed.'

'Good night, Mrs Evans.'

'It won't be after midnight this time, Maud, I promise. I'll put Sambo out in the back.'

'Good night, ma'am.'

Sleep tight, hoity.

'I won't disturb you gentlemen any more,' she said. 'What's left of the parsnip wine for Christmas is in the boot cupboard, Emlyn. Don't let it waste. Good night.'

Mr Evans raised his eyebrows and whistled. 'Whew! boys.' He pretended to fan his face with his tie. Then his hand stopped still in the air. 'She was used to a big house', he said, 'with servants.'

Mr Roberts brought out pencils and fountain pens from his side pocket. 'Where's the priceless MS.? Tempus is fugiting.'

Mr Humphries and Mr Thomas put notebooks on their knees, took a pencil each, and watched Mr Evans open the door of the grandfather clock. Beneath the swinging weights was a heap of papers tied in a blue bow. These Mr Evans placed on the desk.

'I call order,' said Mr Roberts. 'Let's see where we were. Have you got the minutes, Mr Thomas?'

'"*Where Tawe Flows*,"' said Mr Thomas, '"a Novel of Provincial Life. Chapter One: a cross-section description of the town, Dockland, Slums, Suburbia, etc." We finished that. The title decided upon was: Chapter One, "The Public Town". Chapter Two is to be called "The Private Lives", and Mr Humphries has proposed the following: "Each of the collaborators take one character from each social sphere or stratum of the town and introduce him to the readers with a brief history of his life up to the point at which we commence the story, i.e. the winter of this very year. These introductions of the characters, hereafter to be regarded as the principal protagonists, and their biographical chronicles shall constitute the second chapter." Any questions, gentlemen?'

Mr Humphries agreed with all he had said. His character was a sensitive schoolmaster of advanced opinions, who was misjudged and badly treated.

'No questions,' said Mr Evans. He was in charge of Suburbia. He rustled his notes and waited to begin.

'I haven't written anything yet,' Mr Roberts said; 'it's all in my head.' He had chosen the Slums.

'Personally,' said Mr Thomas, 'I haven't made up my mind whether to have a barmaid or a harlot.'

'What about a barmaid who's a harlot too?' Mr Roberts suggested. 'Or perhaps we could have a couple of characters each? I'd like to do an alderman. And a gold-digger.'

'Who had a word for them, Mr Humphries?' said Mr Thomas.

'The Greeks.'

Mr Roberts nudged Mr Evans and whispered: 'I just thought of an opening sentence for my bit. Listen, Emlyn. "On the rickety table in the corner of the crowded, dilapidated room, a stranger might have seen, by the light of the flickering candle in the gin-bottle, a broken cup, full of sick or custard."'

'Be serious, Ted,' said Mr Evans, laughing. 'You wrote that sentence down.'

'No, I swear, it came to me just like that!' He flicked his fingers. 'And who's been reading my notes?'

'Have you put anything on paper yourself, Mr Thomas?'

'Not yet, Mr Evans.' He had been writing, that week, the story of a cat who jumped over a woman the moment she died and turned her into a vampire. He had reached the part of the story where the woman was an undead children's governess, but he could not think how to fit it into the novel.

'There's no need, is there,' he asked, 'for us to avoid the fantastic altogether?'

'Wait a bit! wait a bit!' said Mr Humphries, 'let's get our realism straight. Mr Thomas will be making all the characters Blue Birds before we know where we are. One thing at a time. Has anyone got the history of his character ready?' He had his biography in his hand, written in red ink. The writing was scholarly and neat and small.

'I think my character is ready to take the stage,' said Mr Evans. 'But I haven't written it out. I'll have to refer to the notes and make the rest up out of my head. It's a very silly story.'

'Well, you must begin, of course,' said Mr Humphries with disappointment.

'Everybody's biography is silly,' Mr Roberts said. 'My own would make a cat laugh.'

Mr Humphries said: 'I must disagree there. The life of that mythical common denominator, the man in the street, is dull as ditchwater, Mr Roberts. Capitalist society has made him a mere bundle of repressions and useless habits under that symbol of middle-class divinity, the bowler.' He looked quickly away from the notes in the palm of his hand. 'The ceaseless toil for bread and butter, the ogres of unemployment, the pettifogging gods of gentility, the hollow lies of the marriage bed. Marriage,' he said, dropping his ash on the carpet, 'legal monogamous prostitution.'

'Whoa! whoa! there he goes!'

'Mr Humphries is on his hobby-horse again.'

'I'm afraid,' said Mr Evans, 'that I lack our friend's extensive vocabulary. Have pity on a poor amateur. You're shaming my little story before I begin.'

'I still think the life of the ordinary man is most extraordinary,' Mr Roberts said; 'take my own . . .'

'As the secretary,' said Mr Thomas, 'I vote we take Mr Evans's story. We must try to get *Tawe* finished for the spring list.'

'My *Tomorrow and Tomorrow* was published in the summer in a heat wave,' Mr Humphries said.

Mr Evans coughed, looked into the fire, and began.

'Her name is Mary,' he said, 'but that's not her name really. I'm calling her that because she is a real woman and we don't want any libel. She lives in a house called "Bellevue", but that's not the proper name, of course. A villa by any other name, Mr Humphries. I chose her for my character because her life is a little tragedy, but it's not without its touches of humour either. It's almost Russian. Mary—Mary Morgan now but she was Mary Phillips before she was married and that comes later, that's the anticlimax—wasn't a suburbanite from birth, she didn't live under the shadow of the bowler, like you and me. Or like me, anyway. I was born in "The Poplars" and now I'm in "Lavengro". From bowler to bowler, though I must say, apropos of Mr Humphries's diatribe, and I'm the first to admire his point of view, that the everyday man's just as interesting a character as the neurotic poets of Bloomsbury.'

'Remind me to shake your hand,' said Mr Roberts.

'You've been reading the Sunday papers,' said Mr Humphries accusingly.

'You two argue the toss later on,' Mr Thomas said.

'"Is the Ordinary Man a Mouse?" Now, what about Mary?'

'Mary Phillips,' continued Mr Evans, '—and any more interruptions from the intelligentsia and I'll get Mr Roberts to tell you the story of his operations, no pardons granted—lived on a big farm in Carmarthenshire, I'm not going to tell you exactly where, and her father was a widower. He had any amount of what counts and he drank like a fish, but he was always a gentleman with it. Now, now! forget the class war, I could see it smouldering. He came of a very good, solid family, but he raised his elbow, that's all there is to it.'

Mr Roberts said: 'Huntin', fishin' and boozin'.'

'No, he wasn't quite county and he wasn't a *nouveau riche* either. No Philippstein about him, though I'm not anti-Semite. You've only got to think of Einstein and Freud. There are bad Christians, too. He was just what I'm telling you, if you'd only let me, a man of good farming stock who'd made his pile and now he was spending it.'

'Liquidating it.'

'He'd only got one child, and that was Mary, and she was so prim and proper she couldn't bear to see him the worse for drink. Every night he came home, and he was always the worse, she'd shut herself in her bedroom and hear him rolling about the house and calling for her and breaking the china sometimes. But only sometimes, and he wouldn't have hurt a hair of her head. She was about eighteen and a fine-looking girl, not a film star, mind, not Mr Roberts's type at all, and perhaps she had an Oedipus complex, but she hated her father and she was ashamed of him.'

'What's my type, Mr Evans?'

'Don't pretend not to know, Mr Roberts. Mr Evans

means the sort you can take home and show her your stamp collection.'

'I will have hush,' said Mr Thomas.

''Ave 'ush, is the phrase,' Mr Roberts said. 'Mr Thomas, you're afraid we'll think you're patronizing the lower classes if you drop your aspirates.'

'No nasturtiums, Mr Roberts,' said Mr Humphries.

'Mary Phillips fell in love with a young man whom I shall call Marcus David,' Mr Evans went on, still staring at the fire, avoiding his friends' eyes, and speaking to the burning pictures, 'and she told her father: 'Father, Marcus and I want to be engaged. I'm bringing him home one night for supper, and you must promise me that you'll be sober.'

'He said: "I'm always sober!" but he wasn't sober when he said it, and after a time he promised.

'"If you break your word, I'll never forgive you," Mary said to him.

'Marcus was a wealthy farmer's son from another district, a bit of a Valentino in a bucolic way, if you can imagine that. She invited him to supper, and he came, very handsome, with larded hair. The servants were out. Mr Phillips had gone to a mart that morning and hadn't returned. She answered the door herself. It was a winter's evening.

'Picture the scene. A prim, well-bred country girl, full of fixations and phobias, proud as a duchess, and blushing like a dairymaid, opening the door to her beloved and seeing him standing there on the pitch-black threshold, shy and handsome. This is from my notes.

'Her future hung on that evening as on a thread. "Come in," she insisted. They didn't kiss, but she wanted him to bow and print his lips on her hand. She took him over the house, which had been specially cleaned and polished, and showed him the case with Swansea china in it. There wasn't a portrait gallery, so she showed him the snaps of her mother in the hall and the photograph of her father, tall and young and sober, in the suit he hunted otters in. And all the time she was proudly parading their possessions, attempting to prove to Marcus, whose father was a J.P., that her background was prosperous enough for her to be his bride, she was waiting fearfully the entrance of her father.

'"O God," she was praying, when they sat down to a cold supper, "that my father will arrive presentable." Call her a snob, if you will, but remember that the life of country gentry, or near gentry, was bound and dedicated by the antiquated totems and fetishes of possession. Over supper she told him her family tree and hoped the supper was to his taste. It should have been a hot supper, but she didn't want him to see the servants who were old and dirty. Her father wouldn't change them because they'd always been with him, and there you see the Toryism of this particular society rampant. To cut a long story (this is only the gist, Mr Thomas), they were half way through supper, and their conversation was becoming more intimate, and she had almost forgotten her father, when the front door burst open and Mr Phillips staggered into the passage, drunk as a judge. The dining-room door was ajar and they could see him plainly. I will not try to describe Mary's kaleidoscopic emotions as her father rocked and mumbled in a thick voice in the passage. He was a big man—I forgot to tell you—six foot and eighteen stone.

'"Quick! quick! under the table!" she whispered urgently, and she pulled Marcus by the hand and they crouched under the table. What bewilderment Marcus experienced we shall never know.

'Mr Phillips came in and saw nobody and sat down at the table and finished all the supper. He licked both plates clean, and under the table they heard him swearing and guzzling. Every time Marcus fidgeted, Mary said: "Shhh!"'

'When there was nothing left to eat, Mr Phillips wandered out of the room. They saw his legs. Then, somehow, he climbed upstairs, saying words that made Mary shudder under the table, words of three syllables.'

'Give us three guesses,' said Mr Roberts.

'And she heard him go into his bedroom. She and Marcus crept out of hiding and sat down in front of their empty plates.

'"I don't know how to apologize, Mr David," she said, and she was nearly crying.

'"There's nothing the matter," he said, he was an amenable young man by all accounts, "he's only been to the mart at Carmarthen. I don't like t.t.s myself."

'"Drink makes men sodden beasts," she said.

'He said she had nothing to worry about and that he didn't mind, and she offered him fruit.

'"What will you think of us, Mr David? I've never seen him like that before."

'The little adventure brought them closer together, and soon they were smiling at one another and her wounded pride was almost healed again, but suddenly Mr Phillips opened his bedroom door and charged downstairs, eighteen stone of him, shaking the house.

'"Go away!" she cried softly to Marcus, "please go away before he comes in!"

'There wasn't time. Mr Phillips stood in the passage in the nude.

'She dragged Marcus under the table again, and she covered her eyes not to see her father. She could hear him fumbling in the hall-stand for an umbrella, and she knew what he was going to do. He was going outside to obey a call of nature. "O God," she prayed, "let him find an umbrella and go out. Not in the passage! Not in the passage!" They heard him shout for his umbrella. She uncovered her eyes and saw him pulling the front door down. He tore it off its hinges and held it flat above him and tottered out into the dark.

'"Hurry! please hurry!" she said. "Leave me now, Mr David." She drove him out from under the table.

'"Please, please go now," she said, "we'll never meet again. Leave me to my shame." She began to cry, and he ran out of the house. And she stayed under the table all night.'

'Is that all?' said Mr Roberts. 'A very moving incident, Emlyn. How did you come by it?'

'How can it be all?' said Mr Humphries. 'It doesn't explain how Mary Phillips reached "Bellevue". We've left her under a table in Carmarthenshire.'

'I think Marcus is a fellow to be despised,' Mr Thomas said. 'I'd never leave a girl like that, would you, Mr Humphries?'

'Under a table, too. That's the bit I like. That's a position. Perspectives were different', said Mr Roberts, 'in those days. That narrow puritanism is a spent force. Imagine Mrs Evans under the table. And what happened afterwards? Did the girl die of cramp?'

Mr Evans turned from the fire to reprove him. 'Be as flippant as you will, but the fact remains that an incident like that has a lasting effect on a proud, sensitive girl like Mary. I'm not defending her sensitivity, the whole basis of her pride is outmoded. The social system, Mr Roberts, is not in the box. I'm telling you an incident that occurred. Its social implications are outside our concern.'

'I'm put in my place, Mr Evans.'

'What happened to Mary then?'

'Don't vex him, Mr Thomas, he'll bite your head off.'

Mr Evans went out for more parsnip wine, and, returning, said:

'What happened next? Oh! Mary left her father, of course. She said she'd never forgive him, and she didn't, so she went to live with her uncle in Cardiganshire, a Dr Emyr Lloyd. He was a J.P. too, and rolling in it, about seventy-five—now, remember the age—with a big practice and influential friends. One of his oldest friends was John William Hughes—that's not his name—the London draper, who had a country house near his. Remember what the great Caradoc Evans says? The Cardies always go back to Wales to die when they've rooked the cockneys and made a packet.

'And the only son, Henry William Hughes, who was a nicely educated young man, fell in love with Mary as soon as he saw her and she forgot Marcus and her shame under the table and she fell in love with him. Now don't look disappointed before I begin, this isn't a love story. But they decided to get married, and John William Hughes gave his consent because Mary's uncle was one of the most respected men in the country and her father had money and it would come to her when he died and he was doing his best.

'They were to be married quietly in London. Everything was arranged. Mr Phillips wasn't invited. Mary had her trousseau. Dr Lloyd was to give her away. Beatrice and Betti William Hughes were bridesmaids. Mary went up to London with Beatrice and Betti and stayed with a cousin, and Henry William Hughes stayed in the flat above his father's shop, and the day before the wedding Dr Lloyd arrived from the country, saw Mary for tea, and had dinner with John William Hughes. I wonder who paid for it, too. Then Dr Lloyd retired to his hotel. I'm giving you these trivial details so that you can see how orderly and ordinary everything was. There the actors were, safe and sure.

'Next day, just before the ceremony was to begin, Mary and her cousin, whose name and character are extraneous, and the two sisters, they were both plain and thirty, waited impatiently for Dr Lloyd to call on them. The minutes passed by, Mary was crying, the sisters were sulking, the cousin was getting in everybody's way, but the doctor didn't come. The cousin telephoned the doctor's hotel, but she was told he hadn't spent the night there. Yes, the clerk in the hotel said, he knew the doctor was going to a wedding. No, his bed hadn't been slept in. The clerk suggested that perhaps he was waiting at the church.

'The taxi was ticking away, and that worried Beatrice and Betti, and at last the sisters and the cousin and Mary drove together to the church. A crowd had gathered outside. The cousin poked her head out of the taxi window and asked a policeman to call a churchwarden, and the warden said that Dr Lloyd wasn't there and the groom and the best man were waiting. You can imagine Mary Phillips's feelings when she saw a commotion at the church door and a policeman leading her father out. Mr Phillips had his pockets full of bottles, and how he ever got into the church in the first place no one knew.'

'That's the last straw,' said Mr Roberts.

'Beatrice and Betti said to her: "Don't cry, Mary, the policeman's taking him away. Look! he's fallen in the gutter! There's a splash! Don't take on, it'll be all over soon. You'll be Mrs Henry William Hughes." They were doing their best.

'"You can marry without Dr Lloyd," the cousin told her, and she brightened through her tears—anybody would be crying—and at that moment another policeman——'

'Another!' said Mr Roberts.

'—made his way through the crowd and walked up to the door of the church and sent a message inside. John William Hughes and Henry William Hughes and the best man came out, and they all talked to the policeman, waving their arms and pointing to the taxi with Mary and the bridesmaids and the cousin in it.

'John William Hughes ran down the path to the taxi and shouted through the window: "Dr Lloyd is dead! We'll have to cancel the wedding."

'Henry William Hughes followed him and opened the taxi door and said: "You must drive home, Mary. We've got to go to the police station."

'"And the mortuary," his father said.

'So the taxi drove the bride-to-be home, and the sisters cried worse than she did all the way.'

'That's a sad end,' said Mr Roberts with appreciation. He poured himself another drink.

'It isn't really the end,' Mr Evans said, 'because the wedding wasn't just cancelled. It never came off.'

'But why?' asked Mr Humphries, who had followed the story with a grave expression, even when Mr Phillips fell in the gutter. 'Why should the doctor's death stop everything? She could get someone else to give her away. I'd have done it myself.'

'It wasn't the doctor's death, but where and how he died,' said Mr Evans. 'He died in bed in a bed-sitting-room in the arms of a certain lady. A woman of the town.'

'Kiss me!' Mr Roberts said. 'Seventy-five years old. I'm glad you asked us to remember his age, Mr Evans.'

'But how did Mary Phillips come to live in "Belle-vue"? You haven't told us that,' Mr Thomas said.

'The William Hugheses wouldn't have the niece of a man who died in those circumstances——'

'However complimentary to his manhood,' Mr Humphries said, stammering.

'——marry into their family, so she went back to live with her father and he reformed at once—oh! she had a temper those days—and one day she met a traveller in grain and pigs' food and she married him out of spite. They came to live in "Bellevue", and when Mr Phillips died he left his money to the chapel, so Mary got nothing after all.'

'Nor her husband either. What did you say he travelled in?' asked Mr Roberts.

'Grain and pigs' food.'

After that, Mr Humphries read his biography, which was long and sad and detailed and in good prose; and Mr Roberts told a story about the slums, which could not be included in the book.

Then Mr Evans looked at his watch. 'It's midnight. I promised Maud not after midnight. Where's the cat? I've got to put him out; he tears the cushions. Not that I mind. Sambo! Sambo!'

'There he is, Mr Evans, under the table.'

'Like poor Mary,' said Mr Roberts.

Mr Humphries, Mr Roberts and young Mr Thomas collected their hats and coats from the banister.

'Do you know what time it is, Emlyn?' Mrs Evans called from upstairs.

Mr Roberts opened the door and hurried out.

'I'm coming now, Maud, I'm just saying good night. Good night,' Mr Evans said in a loud voice. 'Next Friday, nine sharp,' he whispered. 'I'll polish my story up. We'll finish the second chapter and get going on the third. Good night, comrades.'

'Emlyn! Emlyn!' called Mrs Evans.

'Good night, Mary,' said Mr Roberts to the closed door.

The three friends walked down the drive.

WHO DO YOU WISH
WAS WITH US?

BIRDS in the Crescent trees were singing; boys on
bicycles were ringing their bells and pedalling down the
slight slope to make the whirrers in their wheels startle
the women gabbing on the sunny doorsteps; small girls
on the pavement, wheeling young brothers and sisters in
prams, were dressed in their summer best and with
coloured ribbons; on the circular swing in the public
playground, children from the snot school spun themselves happy and sick, crying 'Swing us!' and 'Swing us!'
and 'Ooh! I'm falling!'; the morning was as varied and
bright as though it were an international or a jubilee when
Raymond Price and I, flannelled and hatless, with sticks
and haversacks, set out together to walk to the Worm's
Head. Striding along, in step, through the square of the
residential Uplands, we brushed by young men in knife-
creased whites and showing-off blazers, and hockey-
legged girls with towels round their necks and celluloid
sun-glasses, and struck a letterbox with our sticks, and
bullied our way through a crowd of day-trippers who
waited at the stop of the Gower-bound buses, and
stepped over luncheon baskets, not caring if we trod in
them.

'Why can't those bus lizards walk?' Ray said.

'They were born too tired,' I said.

We went on up Sketty Road at a great speed, our
haversacks jumping on our backs. We rapped on every
gate to give a terrific walker's benediction to the people

in the choking houses. Like a breath of fresh air we passed
a man in office pin-stripes standing, with a dog-lead in
his hand, whistling at a corner. Tossing the sounds and
smells of the town from us with the swing of our shoulders
and loose-limbed strides, half-way up the road we heard
women on an outing call 'Mutt and Jeff!' for Ray was tall
and thin and I was short. Streamers flew out of the
charabanc. Ray, sucking hard at his bulldog pipe, walked
too fast to wave and did not even smile. I wondered whom
I had missed among the waving women bowling over the
rise. My love to come, with a paper cap on, might have
sat at the back of the outing, next to the barrel; but,
once away from the familiar roads and swinging towards
the coast, I forgot her face and voice, that had been made
at night, and breathed the country air in.

'There's a different air here. You breathe. It's like the
country,' Ray said, 'and a bit of the sea mixed. Draw it
down; it'll blow off the nicotine.'

He spat in his hand. 'Still town grey,' he said.

He put back the spit in his mouth and we walked on
with our heads high.

By this time we were three miles from the town. The
semi-detached houses, with a tin-roofed garage each and
a kennel in the back plot and a mowed lawn, with sometimes a hanging coconut on a pole, or a bird-bath, or a
bush like a peacock, grew fewer when we reached the
outskirts of the common.

Ray stopped and sighed and said: 'Wait half a sec, I
want to fill the old pipe.' He held a match to it as though
we were in a storm.

Hotfaced and wet-browed, we grinned at each other.
Already the day had brought us close as truants; we were
running away, or walking with pride and mischief,
arrogantly from the streets that owned us into the

unpredictable country. I thought it was against our fate to stride in the sun without the shop-windows dazzling or the music of mowers rising above the birds. A bird's dropping fell on a fence. It was one in the eye for the town. A sheep cried 'Baa!' out of sight, and that would show the Uplands. I did not know what it would show. 'A couple of wanderers in wild Wales,' Ray said, winking, and a lorry carrying cement drove past us towards the golf links. He slapped my haversack and straightened his shoulders. 'Come on, let's be going.' He walked uphill faster than before.

A party of cyclists had pulled up on the roadside and were drinking dandelion and burdock from paper cups. I saw the empty bottles in a bush. All the boys wore singlets and shorts, and the girls wore open cricket shirts and boys' long grey trousers, with safety-pins for clips at the bottoms.

'There's room for one behind, sonny boy,' a girl on a tandem said to me.

'It won't be a stylish marriage,' Ray said.

'That was quick,' I told Ray as we walked away from them and the boys began to sing.

'God, I like this!' said Ray. On the first rise of the dusty road through the spreading heathered common, he shaded his eyes and looked all round him, smoking like a chimney and pointing with his Irish stick at the distant clumps of trees and sights of the sea between them. 'Down there is Oxwich, but you can't see it. That's a farm. See the roof? No, there, follow my finger. This is the life,' he said.

Side by side, thrashing the low banks, we marched down the very middle of the road, and Ray saw a rabbit running. 'You wouldn't think this was near town. It's wild.'

We pointed out the birds whose names we knew, and the rest of the names we made up. I saw gulls and crows, though the crows may have been rooks, and Ray said that thrushes and swallows and skylarks flew above us as we hurried and hummed.

He stopped to pull some blades of grass. 'They should be straws,' he said, and put them in his mouth next to his pipe. 'God, the sky's blue! Think of me, in the G.W.R. when all this is about. Rabbits and fields and farms. You wouldn't think I'd suffered to look at me now. I could do anything, I could drive cows, I could plough a field.'

His father and sister and brother were dead, and his mother sat all day in a wheel-chair, crippled with arthritis. He was ten years older than I was. He had a lined and bony face and a tight, crooked mouth. His upper lip had vanished.

Alone on the long road, the common in the heat mist wasting for miles on either side, we walked on under the afternoon sun, growing thirsty and drowsy but never slowing our pace. Soon the cycling party rode by, three boys and three girls and the one girl on the tandem, all laughing and ringing.

'How's Shanks's pony?'

'We'll see you on the way back.'

'You'll be walking still.'

'Like a crutch?' they shouted.

Then they were gone. The dust settled again. The bells rang faintly through the wood around the road before us. The wild common, six miles and a bit from the town, lay back without a figure on it, and, under the trees, smoking hard to keep the gnats away, we leant against a trunk and talked like men, on the edge of an untrodden place, who have not seen another man for years.

'Do you remember Curly Parry?'

I had seen him only two days ago in the snooker-room, but his dimpled face was fading, even as I thought of him, into the colours of our walk, the ash-white of the road, the common heathers, the green and blue of fields and fragmentary sea, and the memory of his silly voice was lost in the sounds of birds and unreasonably moving leaves in the lack of wind.

'I wonder what he's doing now? He should get out more in the open air, he's a proper town boy. Look at us here.' Ray waved his pipe at the trees and leafy sky. 'I wouldn't change this for High Street.'

I looked at us there; a boy and a young man, with faces, under the strange sunburn, pale from the cramped town, out of breath and hot-footed, pausing in the early afternoon on a road through a popular wood, and I could see the unaccustomed happiness in Ray's eyes and the impossible friendliness in mine, and Ray protested against his history each time he wondered or pointed in the country scene and I had more love in me than I could ever want or use.

'Yes, look at us here,' I said, 'dawdling about. Worm's Head is twelve miles off. Don't you want to hear a tramcar, Ray? That's a wood pigeon. See! The boys are out on the streets with the sports special now. Paper! paper! I bet you Curl's potting the red. Come on! come on!'

'Eyes right!' said Ray, 'I's b——d! Remember that story?'

Up the road and out of the wood, and a double-decker roared behind us.

'The Rhossilli bus is coming,' I said.

We both held up our sticks to stop it.

'Why did you stop the bus?' Ray said, when we were sitting upstairs. 'This was a walking holiday.'

'You stopped it as well.'

We sat in front like two more drivers.

'Can't you mind the ruts?' I said.

'You're wobbling,' said Ray.

We opened our haversacks and shared the sandwiches and hard-boiled eggs and meat paste and drank from the thermos in turns.

'When we get home don't say we took a bus,' I said. 'Pretend we walked all day. There goes Oxwich! It doesn't seem far, does it? We'd have had beards by now.'

The bus passed the cyclists crawling up a hill. 'Like a tow along?' I shouted, but they couldn't hear. The girl on the tandem was a long way behind the others.

We sat with our lunch on our laps, forgetting to steer, letting the driver in his box beneath drive where and how he liked on the switch-back road, and saw grey chapels, and weather-worn angels; at the feet of the hills farthest from the sea, pretty, pink cottages—horrible, I thought, to live in, for grass and trees would imprison me more securely than any jungle of packed and swarming streets and chimney-roosting roofs—and petrol pumps and hay-ricks and a man on a cart-horse standing stock still in a ditch, surrounded by flies.

'This is the way to see the country.'

The bus, on a narrow hill, sent two haversacked walkers bounding to the shelter of the hedge, where they stretched out their arms and drew their bellies in.

'That might have been you and me.'

We looked back happily at the men against the hedge. They climbed on to the road, slow as snails continued walking, and grew smaller.

At the entrance to Rhossilli we pushed the conductor's bell and stopped the bus, and walked, with springing steps, the few hundred yards to the village.

'We've done it in pretty good time,' said Ray.

'I think it's a record,' I said.

Laughing on the cliff above the very long golden beach, we pointed out to each other, as though the other were blind, the great rock of the Worm's Head. The sea was out. We crossed over on slipping stones and stood, at last, triumphantly on the windy top. There was monstrous, thick grass there that made us spring-heeled, and we laughed and bounced on it, scaring the sheep who ran up and down the battered sides like goats. Even on this calmest day a wind blew along the Worm. At the end of the humped and serpentine body, more gulls than I had ever seen before cried over their new dead and the droppings of ages. On the point, the sound of my quiet voice was scooped and magnified into a hollow shout, as though the wind around me had made a shell or cave, with blue, intangible roof and sides, as tall and wide as all the arched sky, and the flapping gulls were made thunderous. Standing there, legs apart, one hand on my hip, shading my eyes like Raleigh in some picture, I thought myself alone in the epileptic moment near bad sleep, when the legs grow long and sprout into the night and the heart hammers to wake the neighbours and breath is a hurricane through the elastic room. Instead of becoming small on the great rock poised between sky and sea. I felt myself the size of a breathing building, and only Ray in the world could match my lovely bellow as I said: 'Why don't we live here always? Always and always. Build a bloody house and live like bloody kings!' The word bellowed among the squawking birds, they carried it off to the headland in the drums of their wings; like a tower, Ray pranced on the unsteady edge of a separate rock and beat about with his stick, which could turn into snakes or flames; and we sank to the ground, the rubbery, gull-limed grass, the sheep-pilled stones, the pieces of bones and feathers, and crouched at the extreme point of the Peninsula. We were still for so long that the dirty-grey gulls calmed down, and some settled near us.

Then we finished our food.

'This isn't like any other place,' I said. I was almost my own size again, five feet five and eight stone, and my voice didn't sweep any longer up to the amplifying sky. 'It could be in the middle of the sea. You could think the Worm was moving, couldn't you? Guide it to Ireland, Ray. We'll see W. B. Yeats and you can kiss the Blarney. We'll have a fight in Belfast.'

Ray looked out of place on the end of the rock. He would not make himself easy and loll in the sun and roll on to his side to stare down a precipice into the sea, but tried to sit upright as though he were in a hard chair and had nothing to do with his hands. He fiddled with his tame stick and waited for the day to be orderly, for the Head to grow paths and for railings to shoot up on the scarred edges.

'It's too wild for a townee,' I said.

'Townee yourself! Who stopped the bus?'

'Aren't you glad we stopped it? We'd still be walking, like Felix. You're just pretending you don't like it here. You were dancing on the edge.'

'Only a couple of hops.'

'I know what it is, you don't like the furniture. There's not enough sofas and chairs,' I said.

'You think you're a country boy; you don't know a cow from a horse.'

We began to quarrel, and soon Ray felt at home again and forgot the monotonous out-of-doors. If snow had fallen suddenly he would not have noticed. He drew down into himself, and the rock, to him, became dark as a house with the blinds drawn. The sky-high shapes that had danced and bellowed at birds crept down to hide, two small town mutterers in a hollow.

I knew what was going to happen by the way Ray lowered his head and brought his shoulders up so that he looked like a man with no neck, and by the way he sucked his breath in between his teeth. He stared at his dusty white shoes and I knew what shapes his imagination made of them; they were the feet of a man dead in bed, and he was going to talk about his brother. Sometimes, leaning against a fence when we watched football, I caught him staring at his own thin hand; he was thinning it more and more, removing the flesh, seeing Harry's hand in front of him, with the bones appearing through the sensitive skin. If he lost the world around him for a moment, if I left him alone, if he cast his eyes down, if his hand lost its grip on the hard, real fence or the hot bowl of his pipe, he would be back in ghastly bedrooms, carrying cloths and basins and listening for handbells.

'I've never seen such a lot of gulls,' I said. 'Have you ever seen such a lot? Such a lot of gulls. You try and count them. Two of them are fighting up there; look, pecking each other like hens in the air. What'll you bet the big one wins? Old dirty beak! I wouldn't like to have had his dinner, a bit of sheep and dead gull.' I swore at myself for saying the word 'dead'. 'Wasn't it gay in town this morning?' I said.

Ray stared at his hand. Nothing could stop him now. 'Wasn't it gay in town this morning? Everybody laughing and smiling in their summer outfits. The kids were playing and everybody was happy; they almost had the band out. I used to hold my father down on the bed when he had fits. I had to change the sheets twice a day for my brother, there was blood on everything. I watched him getting thinner and thinner; in the end you could lift him up with one hand. And his wife wouldn't go to see him because he coughed in her face. Mother couldn't move, and I had to cook as well, cook and nurse and change the sheets and hold father down when he got mad. It's embittered my outlook,' he said.

'But you loved the walk, you enjoyed yourself on the common. It's a wonderful day, Ray. I'm sorry about your brother. Let's explore. Let's climb down to the sea. Perhaps there's a cave with prehistoric drawings, and we can write an article and make a fortune. Let's climb down.'

'My brother used to ring a bell for me; he could only whisper. He used to say: "Ray, look at my legs. Are they thinner today?"'

'The sun's going down. Let's climb.'

'Father thought I was trying to murder him when I held him on the bed. I was holding him down when he died, and he rattled. Mother was in the kitchen in her chair, but she knew he was dead and she started screaming for my sister. Brenda was in a sanatorium in Craigynos. Harry rang the bell in his bedroom when mother started, but I couldn't go to him, and father was dead in the bed.'

'I'm going to climb to the sea,' I said. 'Are you coming?'

He got up out of the hollow into the open world again and followed me slowly over the point and down the steep side; the gulls rose in a storm. I clung to dry, spiked bushes but the roots came out; a foothold crumbled, a crevice for the fingers broke as I groped in it; I scrambled on to a black, flat-backed rock whose head, like a little Worm's, curved out of the sea a few perilous steps away from me, and, drenched by flying water, I gazed up to see Ray and a shower of stones falling. He landed at my side.

'I thought I was done for,' he said, when he had stopped shaking. 'I could see all my past life in a flash.'

'All of it?'

'Well, nearly. I saw my brother's face clear as yours.'

We watched the sun set.

'Like an orange.'

'Like a tomato.'

'Like a goldfish bowl.'

We went one better than the other, describing the sun. The sea beat on our rock, soaked our trouser-legs, stung our cheeks. I took off my shoes and held Ray's hand and slid down the rock on my belly to trail my feet in the sea. Then Ray slid down, and I held him fast while he kicked up water.

'Come back now,' I said, pulling his hand.

'No, no,' he said, 'this is delicious. Let me keep my feet in a bit more. It's warm as the baths.' He kicked and grunted and slapped the rock in a frenzy with his other hand, pretending to drown. 'Don't save me!' he cried. 'I'm drowning! I'm drowning!'

I pulled him back, and in his struggles he brushed a shoe off the rock. We fished it out. It was full of water.

'Never mind, it was worth it. I haven't paddled since I was six. I can't tell you how much I enjoyed it.'

He had forgotten about his father and his brother, but I knew that once his joy in the wild, warm water was over he would return to the painful house and see his brother growing thinner. I had heard Harry die so many times, and the mad father was as familiar to me as Ray himself. I knew every cough and cry, every clawing at the air.

'I'm going to paddle once a day from now on,' Ray said. 'I'm going to go down to the sands every evening and have a good paddle. I'm going to splash about and get wet up to my knees. I don't care who laughs.'

He sat still for a minute, thinking gravely of this. 'When I wake up in the mornings there's nothing to look forward to, except on Saturdays,' he said then, 'or when I come up to your house for Lexicon. I may as well be dead. But now I'll be able to wake up and think: "This evening I'm going to splash about in the sea." I'm going to do it again now.' He rolled up his wet trousers and slid down the rock. 'Don't let go.'

As he kicked his legs in the sea, I said: 'This is a rock at the world's end. We're all alone. It all belongs to us, Ray. We can have anybody we like here and keep everybody else away. Who do you wish was with us?'

He was too busy to answer, splashing and snorting, blowing as though his head were under, making circular commotions in the water or lazily skimming the surface with his toes.

'Who would you like to be here on the rock with us?'

He was stretched out like a dead man, his feet motionless in the sea, his mouth on the rim of a rock pool, his hand clutched round my foot.

'I wish George Gray was with us,' I said. 'He's the man from London who's come to live in Norfolk Street. You don't know him. He's the most curious man I ever met, queerer than Oscar Thomas, and I thought nobody could ever be queerer than that. George Gray wears glasses, but there's no glass in them, only the frames. You wouldn't know until you came near him. He does all sorts of things. He's a cat's doctor and he goes to somewhere in Sketty every morning to help a woman put her clothes on. She's an old widow, he said, and she can't dress by herself. I don't know how he came to know her. He's only been in town for a month. He's a B.A., too.

The things he's got in his pockets! Pincers, and scissors for cats, and lots of diaries. He read me of some the diaries, about the jobs he did in London. He used to go to bed with a policewoman and she used to pay him. She used to go to bed in her uniform. I've never met such a queer man. I wish he was here now. Who do you wish was with us, Ray?'

Ray began to move his feet again, kicking them out straight behind him and bringing them down hard on the water, and then stirring the water about.

'I wish Gwilym was here, too,' I said. 'I've told you about him. He could give a sermon to the sea. This is the very place, there isn't anywhere as lonely as this.' Oh, the beloved sunset! Oh, the terrible sea! Pity the sailors, pity the sinners, pity Raymond Price and me! Oh, the evening is coming like a cloud! Amen. Amen. 'Who do you wish, Ray?'

'I wish my brother was with us,' Ray said. He climbed on to the flat of the rock and dried his feet. 'I wish Harry was here. I wish he was here now, at this moment, on this rock.'

The sun was nearly right down, halved by the shadowed sea. Cold came up, spraying out of the sea, and I could make a body for it, icy antlers, a dripping tail, a rippling face with fishes passing across it. A wind, cornering the Head, chilled through our summer shirts, and the sea began to cover our rock quickly, our rock already covered with friends, with living and dead, racing against the darkness. We did not speak as we climbed. I thought: 'If we open our mouths we'll both say: "Too late, it's too late."' We ran over the spring-board grass and the scraping rock needles, down the hollow in which Ray had talked about blood, up rustling humps, and along the ragged flat. We stood on the beginning of the Head and looked down, though both of us could have said, without looking: 'The sea is in.'

The sea was in. The slipping stepping-stones were gone. On the mainland, in the dusk, some little figures beckoned to us. Seven clear figures, jumping and calling. I thought they were the cyclists.

A PROSPECT OF THE SEA

It was high summer, and the boy was lying in the corn. He was happy because he had no work to do and the weather was hot. He heard the corn sway from side to side above him, and the noise of the birds who whistled from the branches of the trees that hid the house. Lying flat on his back, he stared up into the unbrokenly blue sky falling over the edge of the corn. The wind, after the warm rain before noon, smelt of rabbits and cattle. He stretched himself like a cat, and put his arms behind his head. Now he was riding on the sea, swimming through the golden corn waves, gliding along the heavens like a bird; in seven-league boots he was springing over the fields; he was building a nest in the sixth of the seven trees that waved their hands from a bright, green hill. Now he was a boy with tousled hair, rising lazily to his feet, wandering out of the corn to the strip of river by the hillside. He put his fingers in the water, making a mock sea-wave to roll the stones over and shake the weeds; his fingers stood up like ten tower pillars in the magnifying water, and a fish with a wise head and a lashing tail swam in and out of the tower gates. He made up a story as the fish swam through the gates into the pebbles and the moving bed. There was a drowned princess from a Christmas book, with her shoulders broken and her two red pigtails stretched like the strings of a fiddle over her broken throat; she was caught in a fisherman's net, and the fish plucked her hair. He forgot how the story ended, if ever there were an end to a story that had no beginning. Did the princess live again, rising like a mermaid from the net, or did a prince from another story tauten the tails of her hair and bend her shoulder-bone into a harp and pluck the dead, black tunes for ever in the courts of the royal country? The boy sent a stone skidding over the green water. He saw a rabbit scuttle, and threw a stone at its tail. A fish leaped at the gnats, and a lark darted out of the green earth. This was the best summer since the first seasons of the world. He did not believe in God, but God had made this summer full of blue winds and heat and pigeons in the house wood. There were no chimneys on the hills with no name in the distance, only the trees which stood like women and men enjoying the sun; there were no cranes or coal-tips, only the nameless distance and the hill with seven trees. He could think of no words to say how wonderful the summer was, or the noise of the wood-pigeons, or the lazy corn blowing in the half wind from the sea at the river's end. There were no words for the sky and the sun and the summer country: the birds were nice, and the corn was nice.

He crossed the nice field and climbed the hill. Under the innocent green of the trees, as blackbirds flew out towards the sun, the story of the princess died. That afternoon there was no drowning sea to pull her pigtails; the sea had flowed and vanished, leaving a hill, a cornfield, and a hidden house; tall as the first short tree, she clambered down from the seventh, and stood in front of him in a torn cotton frock. Her bare brown legs were scratched all over, there were berry stains round her mouth, her nails were black and broken, and her toes poked through her rubber shoes. She stood on a hill no bigger than a house, but the field below and the shining strip of river were as little as though the hill were a mountain rising over a single blade and a drop of water; the trees round the farmhouse were firesticks; and the Jarvis peaks, and Cader peak beyond them to the edge of England, were molehills and stones' shadows in the still, single yard of the distance. From the first shade, the boy stared down at the river disappearing, the corn blowing back into the soil, the hundred house trees dwindling to a stalk, and the four corners of the yellow field meeting in a square that he could cover with his hand. He saw the many-coloured county shrink like a coat in the wash. Then a new wind sprang from the pennyworth of water at the river-drop's end, blowing the hill field to its full size, and the corn stood up as before, and the one stalk that hid the house was split into a hundred trees. It happened in a half second.

Blackbirds again flew out from the topmost boughs in a cloud like a cone; there was no end to the black, triangular flight of birds towards the sun; from hill to sun the winged bridge mounted silently; and then again a wind blew up, and this time from the vast and proper sea, and snapped the bridge's back. Like partridges the common birds fell down in a shower.

All of it happened in half a second. The girl in the torn cotton frock sat down on the grass and crossed her legs; a real wind from nowhere lifted her frock, and up to her waist she was brown as an acorn. The boy, still standing timidly in the first shade, saw the broken, holiday princess die for the second time, and a country girl take her place on the live hill. Who had been frightened of a few birds flying out of the trees, and a sudden daze of the sun that made river and field and distance look so little under the hill? Who had told him the girl was as tall as a tree? She was no taller or stranger than the flowery girls on Sundays who picnicked in Whippet valley.

'What were you doing up the tree?' he asked her, ashamed of his silence in front of her smiling, and suddenly shy as she moved so that the grass beneath her rose bent and green between her brown legs. 'Were you after nests?' he said, and sat down beside her. But on the bent grass in the seventh shade, his first terror of her sprang up again like a sun returning from the sea that sank it, and burned his eyes to the skull and raised his hair. The stain on her lips was blood, not berries; and her nails were not broken but sharpened sideways, ten black scissor-blades ready to snip off his tongue. If he cried aloud to his uncle in the hidden house, she would make new animals, beckon Carmarthen tigers out of the mile-away wood to jump around him and bite his hands; she would make new, noisy birds in the air to whistle and chatter away his cries. He sat very still by her left side, and heard the heart in her breast drown every summer sound; every leaf of the tree that shaded them grew to man-size then, the ribs of the bark were channels and rivers wide as a great ship; and the moss on the tree, and the sharp grass ring round the base, were all the velvet coverings of green county's meadows blown hedge to hedge. Now on the world-sized hill, with the trees like heavens holding up the weathers, in the magnified summer weather she leaned towards him so that he could not see the cornfield nor his uncle's house for her thick, red hair; and sky and far ridge were points of light in the pupils of her eyes.

This is death, said the boy to himself, consumption and whooping-cough and the stones inside you . . . and the way your face stays if you make too many faces in the looking-glass. Her mouth was an inch from his. Her long forefingers touched his eyelids. This is a story, he said to himself, about a boy on a holiday kissed by a broom-rider; she flew from a tree on to a hill that changes its size like a frog that loses its temper; she stroked his eyes and put her chest against him; and when she had loved him until he died she carried him off inside her to a den in a wood. But the story, like all stories, was killed as she kissed him; now he was a boy in a girl's arms, and the hill stood above a true river, and the peaks and their trees towards England were as Jarvis had known them when he walked there with his lovers and horses for half a century, a century ago.

Who had been frightened of a wind out of the light swelling the small country? The piece of a wind in the sun was like the wind in an empty house; it made the corners mountains and crowded the attics with shadows who broke through the roof; through the country corridors it raced in a hundred voices, each voice larger than the last, until the last voice tumbled down and the house was full of whispers.

'Where do you come from?' she whispered in his ear. She took her arms away but still sat close, one knee between his legs, one hand on his hands. Who had been frightened of a sunburned girl no taller or stranger than the pale girls at home who had babies before they were married?

'I come from Amman valley,' said the boy.

'I have a sister in Egypt,' she said, 'who lives in a pyramid . . .' She drew him closer.

'They're calling me in for tea,' he said.

She lifted her frock to her waist.

If she loves me until I die, said the boy to himself under the seventh tree on the hill that was never the same for three minutes, she will carry me away inside her, run with me rattling inside her to a den in a wood, to a hole in a tree where my uncle will never find me. This is the story of a boy being stolen. She has put a knife in my belly and turned my stomach round.

She whispered in his ear: 'I'll have a baby on every hill; what's your name, Amman?'

The afternoon was dying; lazily, namelessly drifting westward through the insects in the shade; over hill and tree and river and corn and grass to the evening shaping in the sea; blowing away; being blown from Wales in a wind, in the slow, blue grains, like a wind full of dreams and medicines; down the tide of the sun on to the grey and chanting shore where the birds from Noah's ark glide by with bushes in their mouths, and tomorrow and tomorrow tower over the cracked sand-castles.

So she stroked her clothes into place and patted back her hair as the day began to die, she rolled over on to her left side, careless of the low sun and the darkening miles. The boy awoke cautiously into a more curious dream, a summer vision broader than the one black cloud poised in the unbroken centre on a tower shaft of light; he came out of love through a wind full of turning knives and a cave full of flesh-white birds on to a new summit, standing like a stone that faces the stars blowing and stands no ceremony from the sea wind, a hard boy angry on a mound in the middle of a country evening; he put out his chest and said hard words to the world. Out of love he came marching, head on high, through a cave between two doors to a vantage hall room with an iron view over the earth. He walked to the last rail before pitch space; though the earth bowled round quickly, he saw every plough crease and beast's print, man track and water drop, comb, crest, and plume mark, dust and death groove and signature and time-cast shade, from icefield to icefield, sea rims to sea centres, all over the apple-shaped ball under the metal rails beyond the living doors. He saw through the black thumbprint of a man's city to the fossil thumb of a once-lively man of meadows; through the grass and clover fossil of the country print to the whole hand of a forgotten city drowned under

Europe; through the handprint to the arm of an empire broken like Venus; through the arm to the breast, from history to the thigh, through the thigh in the dark to the first and West print between the dark and the green Eden; and the garden was undrowned, to this next minute and for ever, under Asia in the earth that rolled on to its music in the beginning evening. When God was sleeping, he had climbed a ladder, and the room three jumps above the final rung was roofed and floored with the live pages of the book of days; the pages were gardens, the built words were trees, and Eden grew above him into Eden, and Eden grew down to Eden through the lower earth, an endless corridor of boughs and birds and leaves. He stood on a slope no wider than the loving room of the world, and the two poles kissed behind his shoulders; the boy stumbled forward like Atlas, loped over the iron view through the cave of knives and the capsized overgrowths of time to the hill in the field that had been a short mark under the platform in the clouds over the multiplying gardens.

'Wake up,' she said into his ear; the iron characters were broken in her smile, and Eden shrank into the seventh shade. She told him to look in her eyes. He had thought that her eyes were brown or green, but they were sea-blue with black lashes, and her thick hair was black. She rumpled his hair, and put his hand deep in her breast so that he knew the nipple of her heart was red. He looked in her eyes, but they made a round glass of the sun, and as he moved sharply away he saw through the transparent trees; she could make a long crystal of each tree, and turn the house wood into gauze. She told him her name, but he had forgotten it as she spoke; she told him her age, and it was a new number. 'Look in my eyes,' she said. It was only an hour to the proper night, the stars were coming out and the moon was ready. She took his hand and led him racing between trees over the ridge of the dewy hill, over the flowering nettles and the shut grass-flowers, over the silence into sunlight and the noise of a sea breaking on sand and stone.

The hill in a screen of trees: between the incountry fields and the incoming sea, night on the wood and the stained beach yellow in the sun, the vanishing corn through the ten dry miles of farmland and the golden wastes where the split sand lapped over rocks, it stood between time over a secret root. The hill in two search-lights: the back moon shone on seven trees, and the sun of a strange day moved above water in the spluttering foreground. The hill between an owl and a seagull: the boy heard two birds' voices as brown wings climbed through the branches and the white wings before him fluttered on the sea waves. 'Tu wit tu woo, do not adventure any more.' Now the gulls that swam in the sky told him to race on along the warm sand until the water hugged him to its waves and the spindrift tore around him like a wind and a chain. The girl had her hand in his, and she rubbed her cheek on his shoulder. He was glad of her near him, for the princess was broken, and the monstrous girl was turned into a tree, and the frightening girl who threw the country into a daze of sizes, and drove him out of love into the cloudy house, was left alone in the moon's circle and the seven shades behind the screen.

It was hot that morning in the unexpected sunshine. A girl dressed in cotton put her mouth to his ear. 'I'll run you to the sea,' she said, and her breasts jumped up and down as she raced in front of him, with her hair flying wild, to the edge of the sea that was not made of water and the small, thundering pebbles that broke in a million pieces as the dry sea moved in. Along the bright wrack-line, from the horizon where the vast birds sailed like boats, from the four compass corners, bellying up through the weed beds, melting from orient and tropic, surging through the ice hills and the whale grounds, through sunset and sunrise corridors, the salt gardens and the herring fields, whirlpool and rock pool, out of the trickle in the mountain, down the waterfalls, a white-faced sea of people, the terrible mortal number of the waves, all the centuries' sea drenched in the hail before Christ, who suffered tomorrow's storm wind, came in with the whole world's voices on the endless beach.

'Come back! Come back!' the boy cried to the girl.

She ran on unheeding over the sand and was lost among the sea. Now her face was a white drop of water in the horizontal rainfall, and her limbs were white as snow and lost in the white, walking tide. Now the heart in her breast was a small red bell that rang in a wave, her colourless hair fringed the spray, and her voice lapped over the flesh-and-bone water.

He cried again, but she had mingled with the people moving in and out. Their tides were drawn by a grave moon that never lost an arc. Their long, sea gestures were deliberate, the flat hands beckoning, the heads uplifted, the eyes in the mask faces set in one direction. Oh, where was she now in the sea? Among the white, walking, and the coral-eyed. 'Come back! Come back! Darling, run out of the sea.' Among the processional waves. The bell in her breast was ringing over the sand.

He ran to the yellow foot of the dunes, calling over his shoulder. 'Run out of the sea.' In the once-green water where the fishes swam, where the gulls rested, where the luminous stones were rubbed and rocked on the scales of the green bed, when ships puffed over the tradeways, and the mad, nameless animals came down to drink the salt. Among the measuring people. Oh, where was she now? The sea was lost behind the dunes. He stumbled on over sand and sandflowers like a blind boy in the sun. The sun dodged round his shoulders.

There was a story once upon a time whispered in the water voice; it blew out the echo from the trees behind the beach in the golden hollows, scraped on the wood until the musical birds and beasts came jumping into sunshine. A raven flew by him, out of a window in the Flood to the blind, wind tower shaking in tomorrow's anger like a scarecrow made out of weathers.

'Once upon a time,' said the water voice.

'Do not adventure any more,' said the echo.

'She is ringing a bell for you in the sea.'

'I am the owl and the echo; you shall never go back.'

On a hill to the horizon stood an old man building a boat, and the light that slanted from the sea cast the holy mountain of a shadow over the three-storied decks and the Eastern timber. And through the sky, out of the beds and gardens, down the white precipice built of feathers, the loud combs and mounds, from the caves in the hill, the cloudy shapes of birds and beasts and insects drifted into the hewn door. A dove with a green petal followed in the raven's flight. Cool rain began to fall.

Part III

BROADCASTS

QUITE EARLY ONE MORNING

Quite early one morning in the winter in Wales, by the sea that was lying down still and green as grass after a night of tar-black howling and rolling, I went out of the house, where I had come to stay for a cold unseasonable holiday, to see if it was raining still, if the outhouse had been blown away, potatoes, shears, rat-killer, shrimp-nets, and tins of rusty nails aloft on the wind, and if all the cliffs were left. It had been such a ferocious night that someone in the smoky snipped-pictured bar had said he could feel his tombstone shaking even though he was not dead, or at least was moving; but the morning shone as clear and calm as one always imagines tomorrow will shine.

The sun lit the sea town, not as a whole—from top-most down—reproving zinc-roofed chapel to empty but for rats and whispers grey warehouse on the harbour, but in separate bright pieces. There, the quay shouldering out, nobody on it now but the gulls and the capstans like small men in tubular trousers. Here, the roof of the police-station, black as a helmet, dry as a summons, sober as Sunday. There, the splashed church, with a cloud in the shape of a bell poised above it, ready to drift and ring. Here the chimneys of the pink-washed pub, the pub that was waiting for Saturday night as an over-jolly girl waits for sailors.

The town was not yet awake. The milkman lay still lost in the clangour and music of his Welsh-spoken dreams, the wish-fulfilled tenor voices more powerful than Caruso's, sweeter than Ben Davies's, thrilling past Cloth Hall and Manchester House up to the frosty hills.

The town was not yet awake. Babies in upper bedrooms of salt-white houses dangling over water, or of bow-windowed villas squatting prim in neatly treed but unsteady hill streets, worried the light with their half in sleep cries. Miscellaneous retired sea captains emerged for a second from deeper waves than ever tossed their boats, then drowned again, going down down into a perhaps Mediterranean-blue cabin of sleep, rocked to the sea-beat of their ears. Landladies, shawled and bloused and aproned with sleep in the curtained, bombasined black of their once spare rooms, remember their loves, their bills, their visitors—dead, decamped, or buried in English deserts till the trumpet of next expensive August roused them again to the world of holiday rain, dismal cliff and sand seen through the weeping windows of front parlours, tasselled table-cloths, stuffed pheasants, ferns in pots, fading photographs of the bearded and censorious dead, autograph albums with a lock of limp and colourless beribboned hair lolling out between the thick black boards.

The town was not yet awake. Birds sang in eaves, bushes, trees, on telegraph wires, rails, fences, spars, and wet masts, not for love or joy, but to keep other birds away. The landlords in feathers disputed the right of even the flying light to descend and perch.

The town was not yet awake, and I walked through the streets like a stranger come out of the sea, shrugging off weed and wave and darkness with each step, or like an inquisitive shadow, determined to miss nothing—not the preliminary tremor in the throat of the dawn-saying cock or the first whirring nudge of arranged time in the belly of the alarm clock on the trinketed chest of drawers under the knitted text and the done-by-hand water-colours of Porthcawl or Trinidad.

I walked past the small sea-spying windows, behind whose trim curtains lay mild-mannered men and women not yet awake and, for all I could know, terrible and violent in their dreams. In the head of Miss Hughes, 'The Cosy', clashed the cymbals of an eastern court. Eunuchs struck gongs the size of Bethesda Chapel. Sultans with voices fiercer than visiting preachers demanded a most un-Welsh dance. Everywhere there glowed and rayed the colours of the small, slate-grey woman's dreams, purple, magenta, ruby, sapphire, emerald, vermilion, honey. But I could not believe it. She knitted in her tidy sleep-world a beige woollen shroud with 'thou shalt not' on the bosom.

I could not imagine Cadwallader Davies the grocer in his near-to-waking dream, riding on horseback, two-gunned and Cody-bold, through the cactus prairies. He added, he subtracted, he receipted, he filed a prodigious account with a candle dipped in dried egg.

What big seas of dreams ran in the Captain's sleep? Over what blue-whaled waves did he sail through a rainbow hail of flying-fishes to the music of Circe's swinish island? Do not let him be dreaming of dividends and bottled beer and onions.

Someone was snoring in one house. I counted ten savage and indignant grunts and groans like those of a pig in a model and mudless farm which ended with a window rattler, a wash-basin shaker, a trembler of tooth glasses, a waker of dormice. It thundered with me to the chapel railings, then brassily vanished.

The chapel stood grim and grey, telling the day there was to be no nonsense. The chapel was not asleep, it never cat-napped nor nodded nor closed its long cold eye. I left it telling the morning off and the sea-gull hung rebuked above it.

And climbing down again and up out of the town I heard the cocks crow from hidden farmyards, from old roosts above waves where fabulous sea-birds might sit and cry: 'Neptune!' And a far-away clock struck from another church in another village in another universe, though the wind blew the time away. And I walked in the timeless morning past a row of white cottages almost expecting that an ancient man with a great beard and an hour-glass and a scythe under his night-dressed arm might lean from the window and ask me the time. I would have told him: 'Arise old counter of the heart-beats of albatrosses, and wake the cavernous sleepers of the town to a dazzling new morning.' I would have told him: 'You unbelievable Father of Eva and Dai Adam, come out, old chicken, and stir up the winter morning with your spoon of a scythe.' I would have told him—I would have scampered like a scalded ghost over the cliffs and down to the bilingual sea.

Who lived in these cottages? I was a stranger to the sea town, fresh or stale from the city where I worked for my bread and butter wishing it were laver-bread and country salty butter yolk-yellow. Fishermen certainly; no painters but of boats; no man-dressed women with shooting-sticks and sketch-books and voices like macaws to paint the reluctant heads of critical and sturdy natives who posed by the pint against the chapel-dark sea which would be made more blue than the bay of Naples— though shallower.

I walked on to the cliff path again, the town behind and below waking up now so very slowly; I stopped and turned and looked. Smoke from one chimney—the cobbler's I thought, but from that distance it may have been the chimney of the retired male nurse who had come to live in Wales after many years successful wrestling with

the mad rich of southern England. He was not liked.
He measured you for a strait-jacket carefully with his eye;
he saw you bounce from rubber walls like a sorbo ball.
No behaviour surprised him. Many people of the town
found it hard to resist leering at him suddenly around
the corner, or convulsively dancing, or pointing with
laughter and devilish good humour at invisible dog-
fights merely to prove to him that they were normal.

Smoke from another chimney now. They were burning their last night's dreams. Up from a chimney came
a long-haired wraith like an old politician. Someone
had been dreaming of the Liberal Party. But no, the
smoky figure wove, attenuated into a refined and precise
grey comma. Someone had been dreaming of reading
Charles Morgan. Oh! the town was waking now and I
heard distinctly insistent over the slow-speaking sea the
voices of the town blown up to me. And some of the
voices said:

I am Miss May Hughes 'The Cosy', a lonely lady,
Waiting in her house by the nasty sea,
Waiting for her husband and pretty baby
To come home at last from wherever they may be.

I am Captain Tiny Evans, my ship was the *Kidwelly*,
And Mrs Tiny Evans has been dead for many a year.
'Poor Captain Tiny all alone,' the neighbours whisper,
But I like it all alone and I hated her.

Clara Tawe Jenkins, 'Madam' they call me,
An old contralto with her dressing-gown on,
And I sit at the window and I sing to the sea,
For the sea does not notice that my voice has gone.

Parchedig Thomas Evans making morning tea,
Very weak tea, too, you mustn't waste a leaf.
Every morning making tea in my house by the sea,
I am troubled by one thing only, and that, belief.

Open the curtains, light the fire, what are servants for?
I am Mrs Ogmore Pritchard and I want another snooze.
Dust the china, feed the canary, sweep the drawing-
    room floor;
And before you let the sun in, mind he wipes his shoes.

I am only Mr Griffiths, very short-sighted, B.A., Aber.
As soon as I finish my egg I must shuffle off to school.
O patron saint of teachers, teach me to keep order,
And forget those words on the blackboard—'Griffiths
    Bat is a fool.'

Do you hear that whistling?—It's me, I am Phoebe,
The maid at the King's Head, and I am whistling like
    a bird.
Someone spilt a tin of pepper in the tea.
There's twenty for breakfast and I'm not going to say
    a word.

Thus some of the voices of a cliff-perched town at the
far end of Wales moved out of sleep and darkness into the
new-born, ancient, and ageless morning, moved and were
lost.

A VISIT TO AMERICA

Across the United States of America, from New York to California and back, glazed, again, for many months of the year there streams and sings for its heady supper a dazed and prejudiced procession of European lecturers, scholars, sociologists, economists, writers, authorities on this and that and even, in theory, on the United States of America. And, breathlessly between addresses and receptions, in planes and trains and boiling hotel bedroom ovens, many of these attempt to keep journals and diaries. At first, confused and shocked by shameless profusion and almost shamed by generosity, unaccustomed to such importance as they are assumed, by their hosts, to possess, and up against the barrier of a common language, they write in their notebooks like demons, generalizing away, on character and culture and the American political scene. But, towards the middle of their middle-aged whisk through middle-western clubs and universities, the fury of the writing flags; their spirits are lowered by the spirit with which they are everywhere strongly greeted and which, in ever-increasing doses, they themselves lower; and they begin to mistrust themselves, and their reputations—for they have found, too often, that an audience will receive a lantern-lecture on, say, ceramics, with the same uninhibited enthusiasm that it accorded the very week before to a paper on the Modern Turkish Novel. And, in their diaries, more and more do such entries appear as, 'No way of escape!' or 'Buffalo!' or 'I am beaten', until at last they cannot write a word. And, twittering all over, old before their time, with eyes like rissoles in the sand, they are helped up the gangway of the home-bound liner by kind bosom friends (of all kinds and bosoms) who boister them on the back, pick them up again, thrust bottles, sonnets, cigars, addresses into their pockets, have a farewell party in their cabin, pick them up again, and, snickering and yelping, are gone: to wait at the dockside for another boat from Europe and another batch of fresh, green lecturers.

There they go, every spring, from New York to Los Angeles: exhibitionists, polemicists, histrionic publicists, theological rhetoricians, historical hoddy-doddies, balletomanes, ulterior decorators, windbags, and bigwigs and humbugs, men in love with stamps, men in love with steaks, men after millionaires' widows, men with elephantiasis of the reputation (huge trunks and teeny minds), authorities on gas, bishops, best sellers, editors looking for writers, writers looking for publishers, publishers looking for dollars, existentialists, serious physicists with nuclear missions, men from the B.B.C. who speak as though they had the Elgin Marbles in their mouths, potboiling philosophers, professional Irishmen (very lepri-corny), and I am afraid, fat poets with slim volumes. And see, too, in that linguaceous stream, the tall monocled men, smelling of saddle soap and club arm-chairs, their breath a nice blending of whisky and fox's blood, with big protruding upper-class tusks and county moustaches, presumably invented in England and sent abroad to advertise *Punch*, who lecture to women's clubs on such unlikely subjects as 'The History of Etching in the Shetland Islands'. And the brassy-bossy men-women, with corrugated-iron perms, and hippo hides, who come, self-announced, as 'ordinary British housewives', to talk to rich minked chunks of American matronhood about the iniquity of the Health Services, the criminal sloth of the miners, the *visible* tail and horns of Mr Aneurin Bevan, and the fear of everyone in England to go out alone at night because of the organized legions of cosh boys against whom the police are powerless owing to the refusal of those in power to equip them with revolvers and to flog to ribbons every adolescent offender on any charge at all. And there shiver and teeter also, meek and driven, those British authors unfortunate enough to have written, after years of unadventurous forgotten work, one bad novel which became enormously popular on both sides of the Atlantic. At home, when success first hit them, they were mildly delighted; a couple of literary luncheons went sugar-tipsy to their heads, like the washing sherry served before those luncheons; and perhaps, as the lovely money rolled lushly in, they began to dream in their moony writers' way, of being able to retire to the country, keep wasps (or was it bees?), and never write another lousy word. But in come the literary agent's triggermen and the publisher's armed narks: 'You must go to the States and make a Personal Appearance. Your novel is *killing* them over there, and we're not surprised either. You must go round the States lecturing to women.' And the inoffensive writers, who've never dared lecture anyone, let alone women—they are frightened of women, they do not understand women, they write about women as creatures that never existed, and the women lap it up— these sensitive plants cry out: 'But what shall we lecture about?'

'The English Novel.'

'I don't read novels.'

'Great Women in Fiction.'

'I don't like fiction *or* women.'

But off they're wafted, first class, in the plush bowels

of the *Queen Victoria* with a list of engagements long as a New York menu or a half-hour with a book of Charles Morgan, and soon they are losing their little cold-as-goldfish paw in the great general glutinous handshake of a clutch of enveloping hostesses. I think, by the way, that it was Ernest Raymond, the author of *Tell England*, who once made a journey round the American women's clubs, being housed and entertained at each small town he stopped at by the richest and largest and furriest lady available. On one occasion he stopped at some little station, and was met, as usual, by an enormous motor-car full of a large hornrimmed business man, looking *exactly* like a large hornrimmed business man on the films—and his roly-poly pearly wife. Mr Raymond sat with her in the back of the car, and off they went, the husband driving. At once she began to say how utterly delighted she and her husband and the committee were to have him at their Women's Literary and Social Guild, and to compliment him on his books. 'I don't think I've ever, in all my life, enjoyed a book so much as *Sorrel and Son*', she said. 'What you don't know about human nature! I think Sorrel is one of the most beautiful characters ever portrayed.'

Ernest Raymond let her talk on, while he stared, embarrassed, in front of him. All he could see were the three double chins that her husband wore at the back of his neck. On and on she gushed in praise of *Sorrel and Son* until he could stand it no longer. 'I quite agree with you,' he said. 'A beautiful book indeed. But I'm afraid I didn't write *Sorrel and Son*. It was written by an old friend of mine, Mr Warwick Deeping.'

And the large hornrimmed double-chinned husband at the wheel said without turning: 'Caught again, Emily.'

See the garrulous others, also, gabbing and garlanded from one nest of culture-vultures to another: people selling the English way of life and condemning the American way as they swig and guzzle through it; people resurrecting the theories of surrealism for the benefit of remote parochial female audiences who did not know it was dead, not having ever known it had been alive; people talking about Etruscan pots and pans to a bunch of dead pans and wealthy pots in Boston. And there, too, in the sticky thick of lecturers moving across the continent black with clubs, go the foreign poets, catarrhal troubadours, lyrical one-night-standers, dollar-mad nightingales, remittance-bards from at home, myself among them booming with the worst.

Did we pass one another, *en route*, all unknowing, I wonder, one of us, spry-eyed, with clean, white lectures and a soul he could call his own, going buoyantly west to his remunerative doom in the great State University factories, another returning dog-eared as his clutch of poems and his carefully typed impromptu asides? I ache for us both. There one goes, unsullied as yet, in his Pullman pride, toying, oh boy, with a blunderbuss bourbon, being smoked by a large cigar, riding out to the wide open spaces of the faces of his waiting audience. He carries, besides his literary baggage, a new, dynamic razor, just on the market, bought in New York, which operates at the flick of a thumb, but cuts the thumb to the bone; a tin of new shaving-lather which is worked with the other, unbleeding, thumb and covers not only the face but the whole bathroom and, instantly freezing, makes an arctic, icicled cave from which it takes two sneering bell-boys to extract him; and, of course, a nylon shirt. This, he dearly believed from the advertisements, he could himself wash in his hotel, hang to dry overnight, and put on, without ironing, in the morning. (In my case, no ironing *was* needed, for, as someone cruelly pointed out in print, I looked, anyway, like an unmade bed.)

He is vigorously welcomed at the station by an earnest crew-cut platoon of giant collegiates, all chasing the butterfly culture with net, note-book, poison-bottle, pin, and label, each with at least thirty-six terribly white teeth, and is nursed away, as heavily gently as though he were an imbecile rich aunt with a short prospect of life, into a motor-car in which, for a mere fifty miles or so travelled at poet-breaking speed, he assures them of the correctness of their assumption that he is half-witted by stammering inconsequential answers in an over-British accent to their genial questions about what international conference Stephen Spender might be attending at the moment or the reactions of British poets to the work of a famous American whose name he did not know or catch. He is then taken to a small party of only a few hundred people all of whom hold the belief that what a visiting lecturer needs before he trips on to the platform is just enough martinis so that he can trip *off* the platform as well. And, clutching his explosive glass, he is soon contemptuously dismissing, in a flush of ignorance and fluency, the poetry of those androgynous literary ladies with three names who produce a kind of verbal ectoplasm to order as a waiter dishes up spaghetti—only to find that the fiercest of these, a wealthy huntress of small, seedy lions (such as himself), who stalks the middle-western bush with ears and rifle cocked, is his hostess for the evening. Of the lecture he remembers little but the applause and maybe two questions: 'Is it true that the young English intellectuals are *really* psychological?' or, 'I always carry Kierkegaard in my pocket. What do you carry?'

Late at night, in his room, he fills a page of his journal with a confused, but scathing, account of his first engagement; summarizes American advanced education in a paragraph that will be meaningless tomorrow, and falls to sleep where he is immediately chased through long, dark thickets by a Mrs Mabel Frankincense Mehaffey, with a tray of martinis and lyrics.

And there goes the other happy poet bedraggedly back to New York which struck him all of a sheepish never-sleeping heap at first but which seems to him now, after the ulcerous rigours of a lecturer's spring, a haven cosy at toast, cool as an icebox, and safe as skyscrapers.

The Public Eye

A PORT CITY HIGH NOVEL

SHANNON FREEMAN

SADDLEBACK
PUBLISHING

High School High

Taken

Deported

The Public Eye

www.sdlback.com

ISBN-13: 978-1-62250-040-6
ISBN-10: 1-62250-040-7
eBook: 978-1-61247-683-4

Printed in Guangzhou, China
NOR/1113/CA21302125

18 17 16 15 14   1 2 3 4 5

ACKNOWLEDGMENTS

$\mathcal{I}$ feel that I need to thank my family for being so supportive. Whether you are purchasing books or showing up to book signings, it is appreciated. Being one of the youngest in my family, I have always felt your support and love no matter where my heart's desires have taken me. A special thanks to the Warrick family, Ford family, Freeman family, Francis family, Loivolette family, and Woods family. I have a small piece of each one of you in me.

Arianne McHugh, you changed my life. Thank you so much for having an open mind and helping me navigate through this new world. You are an awesome tour guide. I hope I live up to all of your expectations. I know that you went out on a limb for me. I am forever indebted to you.

Thank you to everyone who has read any of my books and taken the time to write me and let me know how much you enjoyed it. Your words of encouragement have been so touching. I'm still so new to all of this and shocked each time I open a card, a letter, an e-mail, or read a post. You have no idea how much you bless my life.

Thanks again,

Shannon

DEDICATION

They say behind every good man is a good woman. Well, behind every good woman, there's a good mother, and I truly have the best. At the end of the day, when I've poured everything I have into everyone else, you make sure that I have all my needs met. Thank you for always thinking of me. I don't know where I would be without you.

Prologue

After their annual New Year's party, the girls were optimistic about the year ahead. All of their families were in a good place. Even the Maldonados, who had dealt with some serious issues last semester, were doing much better.

Marisa's brother, Romero, had gotten into some trouble, and their father's sudden outburst during Romero's court appearance had left him incarcerated and facing deportation. If it hadn't been for Shane's father putting his neck on the line, their story would have ended much differently.

Brian Foster had been the driving force behind Mr. Maldonado's release. He had asked for some favors, and now it was Mr. Foster's turn to make good on the promises he had made to some of Port City's most influential people.

And then there was Brandi's father, who had just gotten out of rehab. The Haywoods were all experiencing some difficulties adjusting to his return, but for the most part, they were just happy he was back home and in a good frame of mind.

"I am *not* ready to go back to school," Shane had declared, lying across the bed and dreading the conclusion of Christmas break.

"Me neither. It's too cold outside, and I just want to stay in bed. Christmas break should be as long as summer break. Wouldn't that be nice?" Marisa responded.

"If it wasn't for basketball season, I would just homeschool this semester," Brandi said, laughing.

"Yeah right, we are too fly to be locked up in the house all day," Shane told them. "I wonder what time Ryan's picking me up. I need to text him."

"Dude, how many boyfriends are you gonna have this year?" Brandi asked Shane as they waited for Ryan Petry to pick her up for their date.

"I don't have a boyfriend. Ryan is just a friend who asked me out on a date."

"Um-hm, tell me anything. He is kind of cute, though, in a hot-bookworm kind of way. Ashton is going to be so upset," Brandi chuckled. "Just don't go anyplace where he may see you."

"I am not running from Ashton either. He is just my friend."

"No ... I'm your friend. Marisa's your friend."

"Amen to that!" Marisa hollered from

the bathroom, where she was flat ironing her hair.

"Ryan and Ashton drool when you're anywhere near them. What friends do that?" Brandi asked.

"This is a new year and a new me. I'm just trying to be more open to what's out there. You know I don't really date," Shane told them.

"Oh, so we are on New Year's resolutions now?" Brandi asked.

"I'm down," Marisa hollered from the bathroom. "Gimme a sec." Marisa finished her hair and joined her friends in Shane's bedroom.

"I already know what I have to do this year," Brandi told them. "I have to decide where this thing with Bryce is going. I was so sure before, but now … I-D-K."

"Yeah, I'm with you, B. Pump your brakes with that one. The thing is, my girl Brandi Haywood can stand on her own two feet. Bryce ain't the reason you still standing ... you are."

Shane knew this was the best moment to tell Brandi how she felt about her relationship with Bryce Thomas. He was a hot-headed kid with a lot of baggage. She had met him in a group for troubled teens, and he was not only troubled, Shane felt he was disturbed.

Brandi nodded her head in agreement. "I know what you're saying, sis. I see it too. Don't think I'm blind."

"Okay, my turn," Marisa told them. "This year I'm focusing on modeling. Somehow, some way, a door is going to open for me. I can just feel it."

"That sounds good to me," Brandi told her. "You've got that *something special*, and somebody's gonna recognize it. You just gotta grind it out. Whatever that means, for wherever you are."

The girls held hands, and each of them

prayed silently for the upcoming year, for their families, and for their goals. Shane stuck her arm out in the middle of the circle. Brandi and Marisa followed suit. "New year, new me," she declared. "Better yet, new year, new we."

"I like that," Marisa said, giving her a nod of approval. "New year, new we."

Brandi repeated it as well, with a smile on her face. "I like it too. Adding it to my timeline today."

"Girl, you need to make a no-Friender resolution," Shane told her. After Brandi's abduction in ninth grade, the girls were all skeptical—and very cautious—about social networking. "You just be careful. And promise us, no Internet dating, please. We just got you back."

"I'm not trying to date anybody, but I like Friender. And that creep, Steven, is not going to have me scared of using my own computer. I won't give him that much power," Brandi declared. "Now let's get back to PCH and rock out the end of this sophomore year."

"That's what I'm talking about," Shane agreed.

CHAPTER 1

Shane

*I*t was cold outside. It had rained for the past two days, so to get a little break from the rain was a pleasant surprise. Today, there wasn't a cloud in the sky. It was a beautiful, crisp winter afternoon. Even the birds had come out to enjoy the sunshine.

Shane wanted to look smart and sophisticated. After all, she knew that Ryan would look like a reporter straight out of the *Port City Tribune* when he arrived. Ryan was a serious twelfth grader, the editor-in-chief of the school newspaper and yearbook, and her boss in her position as photo editor. She wasn't sure what he wanted with a sophomore, but she seemed to intrigue him.

"Hey," Shane said as she jumped into Ryan's Jeep Cherokee. It was an older model, but it was in good shape. She could tell that the radio had been upgraded with an XM system. His truck was comfortable and warm and seemed perfect for him.

"Hey, Shane. I hate to be rude. I should say hello to your parents."

"They aren't even home right now. They had a meeting or something downtown. So no worries. And what do you have planned for us today?"

"You mean Shane Foster is going to let me take the lead on this date? Cool."

"Of course. I know how to ride shotgun."

"Well, in that case, I thought we'd go by the museum for lunch."

"The museum? We are not that old, Ryan. Haven't you heard of burgers and a movie?"

"Girl, didn't you just say that you know how to ride shotgun? Well then, ride."

"You're right, but this better be good. I didn't even know Port City had a museum."

When they arrived at the museum, there was a sign for the current exhibition. It read *Real People, Places, and Faces*, Exhibit Hall B. They followed the directions to Exhibit Hall B, and Shane gasped at the entrance. She looked at Ryan, who watched her as she realized what her eyes were taking in: display after display of work by famous Texas photographers.

Before her was the work of area photographers she admired. The images were powerful. A tribute to the vast Texas landscape. Photographs of aging architecture, old fishing boats, abandoned churches, traditional Mexican weddings, oilmen, cattle ranchers, and rodeos. Quiet photos of mothers and babies. Landscapes of the lone star sky in a series of large panels.

Shane soaked it all in. These artists

were every bit as good as Ansel Adams, Annie Liebovitz, Irving Penn. And these Texans had done it all on film too. She was gobsmacked. She couldn't wrap her brain around film the way she had with digital. It was eye-opening. Mesmerizing. Inspirational. "How did you know this was here? It's everything," she said, never taking her eyes off the work in front of her. "I just wish I had my own camera with me."

Ryan pulled a camera from the bag that he was carrying. "I thought you might say that."

She snapped pictures of the pictures on the wall to document her experience, flash off, of course. By the end of the exhibit, she was emotionally drained. "This was euphoric, Ryan. Thank you so much. I want to come back every day until my own work is on that wall."

"Keep going like you're going and it will be. You have talent, Shane."

Shane couldn't believe that she had never seen Ryan before. Well, she did meet him last year, but she didn't *see* him. This was different. "So what do you have planned for me next?" she asked, more interested than before.

"There's lunch available in the courtyard over there. I was thinking that we could grab some food and a latte or something. They have great shrimp tacos, but you can get whatever you like. You've been a pretty cheap date up until this point," he joked.

"Well, you've been a pretty cheap host, taking me to a free exhibit," she said, nudging him in the side. "But I trust you. If you say the shrimp tacos are great, then I'll give them a shot. You were certainly right about coming to the museum. The exhibit was amazing!"

Shane grabbed a seat in the middle of the courtyard. It was a quaint little area where food carts were lined up and connected by Christmas lights. There were heat lamps in the eating area that kept it nice and toasty.

Shane remembered seeing all kinds of food carts and trucks on her last visit to Austin. The Texas capital had a happening food scene. She saw carts set up in parking lots and on sidewalks—in groups or as stand-alones. They were everywhere. The Fosters had not eaten as well in some of the fancier restaurants in Port City as they had that weekend in Austin. There were gourmet hot dogs, tacos, Vietnamese pho, crepes, cupcakes, puffy tacos, po'boys, gumbo ... You name it, you could find it on a food cart.

And now the carts were popping up all over Port City. But finding them was hit or miss. Who knew the stuffy museum was the place to be for great food? While her hometown had not reached the sophisticated heights of Austin, Shane did see a variety of interesting foods to sample in the future. There was a food cart called Oink. And who didn't love pork in all its forms? She made a mental note to try that one later. Another cart seemed to only serve biscuits. And another was called Chill. Homemade ice cream! She was definitely coming back when the temperature warmed up. Her crew was going to eat this up. Literally.

Ryan brought her a white chocolate mocha first so that she could keep warm while her tacos were being prepared. The contrast of the cold air and the hot drink made the steam rise from the cup and dance. The smell of white chocolate tickled her nose. *What an amazing day,* she thought.

Ryan arrived back at the table with their food. The shrimp was blackened to perfection and wrapped in a homemade tortilla filled with cabbage and a secret sauce to die for. "Oh my," Shane said after taking her first bite. "I've never had shrimp tacos this good before."

"Try adding some lime juice."

She squeezed a lime wedge over her taco and took a huge bite. "Why is this so good? Now you're going to have me eating at the museum once a week," she laughed.

"Pretty impressive for little ole Port City, right?" he asked.

"Ryan," she said between bites of taco, "I haven't had food this yummy since my dad took us all to Austin after school got out. They have food carts galore there. I knew we were starting to get some in Port City, but I never thought we'd see anything like this. It's amazing. Brandi and Mari are going to totally flip when I tell them about it."

Shane licked her lips. She looked at Ryan through new eyes. She had seriously misjudged him as geeky and boring. Last year he wasn't even a blip on her radar. But as she peeled back the layers, she saw a guy who had a lot going on.

"Hey, we can hang out here anytime you like. Is your dad ready for the election campaigning to start?"

Just the thought of the election put Shane on pause. "I don't know. I mean, I'm happy for my dad. I'm just nervous. There's a lot about me that you don't know, and I don't want it to be public knowledge either."

"Like what?"

"Nothing, Ryan." There was an awkward silence between them. It had been the first one all day. Ryan regretted bringing up the election. He hadn't wanted to ruin their date.

"I had fun today," he said.

"Me too. Thank you so much. I would have never experienced any of this if it wasn't for you." She could hear her phone vibrating in her purse.

"Wanna hang?" It was a text from Ashton. Her face must have changed because Ryan asked her what was wrong.

"I'm fine," she said. She looked around at where she was. *Ashton would hate it here*, she thought. "Just fine."

"Good, let's get you home. It's getting cold out here."

CHAPTER 2

Marisa

After Mr. Maldonado was released from jail, he tried desperately to get his construction business back up to speed, but his client list was looking very skimpy. Many of his customers switched to his competitors, and he was finding it increasingly difficult to pick up more during the winter when nobody seemed to want to remodel or repair anything. The steady income that flowed into their house wasn't there anymore.

"What are we going to do?" he asked his wife, feeling more nervous than ever.

"Well, first of all, I've added a few new houses to my cleaning service. That should help out a little bit, but I can only clean so much. My hands are starting to ache," she complained to her husband.

"I wouldn't dream of having you take on more than you can handle. I have to find something for myself. That's all."

"You can always try the refinery. I'm sure you can do something there. Can we call somebody?"

"I don't know. They only seem interested in people coming from out of town these days. The climate at the refinery is changing. It's harder to get in, and I hate working for other people. I'm used to having my own business."

"But that's not working for us right now, George. You have to adjust."

"I know. I know."

Marisa could hear everything her parents were saying in the living room. She wasn't trying to eavesdrop. The house was just so quiet today. Their conversation made her nervous. She knew she had to do something to help.

Marisa immediately got online to find out where she could get work. She knew if she obtained a work permit, she could find a job at any of the local fast-food spots. She dreamed of the day when she could make her own money working at a clothing store.

Not only did she love modeling, but she adored fashion. Her passion began years ago when her mother would bring home fashion magazines given to her by her clients. *Vogue, Essence, Elle, Marie Claire* .... They had already been read; it was thoughtful of her mom's clients to pass them on. Why not give them away for someone else to enjoy? And with three daughters at home, Mrs. Maldonado knew they wouldn't go to waste.

Marisa stopped scanning the jobs list the moment her eyes fell on the notice for an open call for models for Gap clothing stores.

"An open call? Right here in Port City?" Marisa said to herself. She knew that she *had* to be there. The date for the open call wasn't until February. That was good. It gave her over a month to prepare. She knew she had to get started right away with eating right and working out.

She was already thin, and she didn't want to look anorexic, but her body could use some toning. And really, Marisa told herself, she could stand to lose a few pounds—since everybody knew the camera added ten. But she wanted to do it in a healthy way.

Her head was in the clouds, dreaming about the day of the open call. She had visions of showing up and being whisked past the other girls who had been waiting for hours. She'd be discovered on the spot and moved to the front of the line.

She knew she had to assemble the perfect outfit. She needed to look like she had just stepped out of a Gap ad. She was a girl on a mission. She was determined for it to work out, not only for her but for her family.

CHAPTER 3

Brandi

Everyone, please take out your protractors now," Mr. Mutomba instructed the class. He drew a half circle on the board and marked off angles, labeling them obtuse, right, and acute. "I'll need you to be able to differentiate these three types of angles. You'll have a quiz over this lesson on Friday."

"Com 2 rr," flashed on Brandi's phone. It was Bryce. Her face lit up at the anticipation of getting away from this boring lesson and going to see her boo. Her hand shot up in the air as soon as she read it.

"Yes, Brandi, you have a question,"

Mr. Mutomba asked in his thick African accent.

"Yes, sir, may I please be excused to go to the restroom. It's an emergency."

"Just take the restroom pass off my desk. Anymore questions at this time?" he asked, scanning the room. "Okay, turn to page three fifty-six in your text. There are ten practice questions on that page. You'll be responsible for all of them."

Brandi could hear his instructions as she left the room. She rolled her eyes, knowing that she would have to make up the assignment when she returned. It was enough to make her not want to come back at all.

"Hey, you," she said as she approached Bryce in the empty hallway. His face always made her pause. He was absolutely gorgeous. *How did I get so lucky?* she thought. This kid was naturally tanned and had the most amazing curly hair. His Dickies were starched and sagged just the right amount. The contrast of his light blue polo against his skin gave Brandi butterflies.

He was such a pretty boy. And Brandi had a weakness for the pretty ones. She knew she had a type. But she had also learned that she was not the best judge of character. As she took in the eye candy, her heart thumped away. But red flags were trying to wake up her sluggish head.

It was too soon to be with anyone, and she knew it. But she dismissed those silly thoughts as soon as they came up. Bryce was exactly what she needed. At least that's what she wanted to believe. "What took you so long?" he asked, agitated.

"Here we go. I was in *class*, Bryce. I had to get permission to leave. You should have sent the text *before* you left class instead of from the restroom."

"Girl, watch your mouth! Don't tell me what I should have done. Just get your big behind out here when I text you."

"Whatever, Bryce, I don't even know why I left class for you. You make me sick," she huffed. She folded her arms and dug her heels into the floor. She was not going to give in to this boy.

"Oh, I make you sick, huh? Girl, you know you love me. Now come give me a kiss before my teacher gets mad that I've been gone so long."

"I don't wanna kiss yo' stank behind, Bryce."

"Yeah, you do," he said, pulling her close to him. Even though she didn't want to, she melted in his arms. "See, I told you," he said breathlessly. He kissed her like she belonged to him, and she loved every moment. "Now next time, don't keep me waiting," he said, slapping her on the butt.

"Boy, stop," she said right as the assistant principal came around the corner.

"Is there a problem here?" he asked Brandi.

"No, sir. I was just heading back to class. I had to use the restroom."

"Good," he said, giving Bryce the once-over.

Everyone was a little more protective of Brandi since her abduction last spring. Mr. Spears was no different. The school had held candlelight vigils. Counselors had been called in to deal with emotional students. Her photograph had been plastered all over the campus.

"Where are you headed, son?" Mr. Spears asked.

"I'm not your son," Bryce said, snapping at Mr. Spears. "I am going to class."

"Fair enough, young man, but talking to people the way you do tells me that whoever *does* claim you as a son isn't teaching you much at home."

Brandi braced herself. She knew that Mr. Spears had hit Bryce's weak spot: his parents.

"What did you say?" Bryce asked slowly.

Brandi tried to stop him. "Come on, Bryce. Let's go to class. Bye, Mr. Spears," she said, pulling Bryce down the hall.

"Girl! Let go of me," he told her.

"No, you are going to class before you get in trouble. Bryce! Look at me! You have to chill. I know what he said pushed your buttons, but he's the assistant principal. Chill!" she said, looking him eye-to-eye.

"I'ma chill now, but it ain't over with that fool," he warned her.

Brandi was getting tired of trying to save him from himself. She felt like her mother. It was the same thing that she was trying to do with her dad, save him from himself.

"I know, baby," she said, giving him a peck on the lips to calm him down.

As soon as she returned to class, Brandi began gathering her things. Mr. Mutomba checked the clock and shook his head.

"Miss Haywood," he said, "I expect you to turn in those ten practice questions tomorrow."

Just then, the bell rang. Mr. Mutomba approached her as she tried to slink out of the room. "What took you so long? You missed a great deal of instruction."

"I'm sorry, Mr. Mutomba. I had feminine problems," she said and smiled, showing her beautiful white teeth. She could tell she'd made her teacher uncomfortable, and she felt a little twinge of guilt watching his reaction.

"Oh ... okay ... carry on, then," he said nervously.

CHAPTER 4

Campaign Kickoff

The Pier was a plush room donned with chandeliers, a dining area, a full chef's kitchen, and a posh seating area with soft couches designed for mingling. It was the perfect location for Mr. Foster's announcement party. It would be the first fundraiser of his campaign. Everyone who was anyone in the city had been invited. Outfits had been purchased by Mrs. Foster for Robin, Shane, and Aiden. They looked like the picture-perfect family. Standing in front of their friends and family, nobody would have known that their home had been a chaotic nightmare only hours before.

"I'm not wearing that stupid dress," Shane told her mother. "Where did you buy that anyway, Sears?"

"Shane, just wear the dress. You'll look fine," Robin told her. "Plus, Mom has us all in the same colors, so it'll look good when we're all together. This is about Dad, not you."

"Shane, I'm warning you, put the dress on before you make us late," her mother scolded her.

Shane looked at the clothes in disgust. There was no personality, and everyone was too matchy-matchy in navy blue and red. Who would wear that? All she needed were white gloves and little Sunday hat to complete her nerd look.

"You have us dressed like dweebs, and I'm not looking like that in front of my friends. No way."

"What's the problem?" her dad shouted, catching her off guard.

"Nothing, I'm just not wearing this dress. Look at me, Dad. If I have to wear it, then I'm not going."

"All of this is over a dress? You have to be kidding me. I'm a nervous wreck, and I have to break up an argument over clothing. Put the dress on now or else you won't see the light of day when this is over. Am I clear?" His voice was growing louder, but Shane still didn't respond. When she got into one of her moods, there was no reasoning with her. "Am I clear, Shane?" he yelled.

"Huh?" She had used that word since she was two years old. When asked a question that she didn't want to answer, *huh* was her go-to response.

"Don't play with me, Shane," Mr. Foster

had warned her and left the room. He knew continuing to argue with her would get them nowhere, but she knew when he returned that dress had better be on her body.

All eyes were on the Foster family that day. While Brian Foster was busy mingling with his guests, all of the major news stations were arriving. They were all prepared to document his run for the Area 14 seat. Hundred dollar bills were being put in his hands as he moved through the crowd, shaking hands with his guests. "You and your family are a great representation of our city, Mr. Foster," Joann Marks, a former council member, told him, pulling out her checkbook. She wrote a five hundred dollar check.

"Mrs. Marks, this is too much."

"Honey, it's never too much, especially when you are running against a snake like Stringer," she said in her perfect southern drawl. She had been on the council for years but gave up her seat when her husband became ill.

You would have never known she was eighty-two years old. She was a tall, regal older lady with impeccably styled salt-and-pepper hair. In her former life, she was a businesswoman. She and her husband owned a thriving swimming pool company. With time on her hands, she became a motivational speaker, and that took on a life of its own. She was still one of Port City's most sought-after speakers. When her husband was diagnosed with cancer, they decided it was time to slow down, travel, and enjoy each other.

Now, the only politics that she involved herself with was giving, and she was very generous. "If you ever need anything, Mr. Foster, please do not hesitate to call me."

Brian Foster was surprised he had so much support, but not as surprised as his family.

"Is Dad going to be famous now?" Shane asked Robin.

"You are so young sometimes. Yeah, sure, he'll be famous in Port City."

"Well, dang, I'm famous too, then."

"Go talk to Marisa and Brandi. Your conversations are stupid."

"You're stupid. Give me Aiden. I want my nephew." Shane went from table to table talking to her friends. Marisa, Brandi, Trent, and Ashton sat at one table, and Ryan and most of the journalism department were one table over. Shane stopped to talk to her friends from journalism first.

"Is this your nephew?" one of the girls gushed.

"Yeah, this is Aiden." He smiled that beautiful Foster smile, showing his gums.

"Hey, I didn't want to have them just start taking pictures without your permission, but we can get some great shots for the campaign if you like," Ryan told her.

"That sounds great, Ryan. You are awesome," she said, hugging him.

Ashton's ears immediately perked up when he heard Shane. He knew Ryan was making a move in her direction, and he was upset that she was even entertaining the idea of dating him. Ashton and Ryan had been in the same classes since middle school. They were two totally different people, and he just couldn't believe he was competing with *him* for Shane's attention.

By the time Shane arrived at her best friends' table, heat was rising off of Ashton, making him uncharacteristically quiet.

"Hey, hey, hey ... where my peoples at?" she asked, joking with her friends. Ashton immediately got up from the table and walked to the other room. "What's with your boy?" she asked Trent.

"You know what's with him," Trent told her.

"Girl, what you wearing?" Brandi

snorted. "Looks like your mom went to Gymboree for teenagers."

"Hey, now," Shane started to say, then she rolled her eyes. "I was threatened. I could stay in the house forever, or wear this stupid sack. Here, take Aiden for a second," she said to Marisa.

"Hey, why does she get to keep Aiden," Brandi complained, but Shane was already gone and trying to find Ashton.

She searched the seating area, but he was nowhere to be found. She peeked in every nook and cranny in the whole building, but she couldn't find him. Just when she was about to give up, she noticed him pass by the door. He was outside and heading toward his car.

"Ash, where are you going? Come back inside. It's freezing out here."

"Nah, I'm good, Shane. Go back in there with your dude and them."

"What?" she asked, confused.

"Ryan Petry, you know who I'm talking about. Stop playing, Shane."

"It's not like that, Ashton," she whined. She didn't even know why she was standing in the cold trying to reason with him. She hadn't made a commitment to either one of them, but she still had drama.

"Look, I know that we ain't like that. You don't have to be out here trying to make me feel better. It's all good, Shane," he said, taking both of her hands in his. "I'm the one with the problem. I was the one who started wanting you, not the other way around."

"Ash, I'm sorry. I don't know what to say. Things may be different if I was looking to be wifed, but that's not where I'm at right now."

"So, are you telling Nerd Alert in there the same thing?" he asked, looking down at her intently.

"Don't be mean or nosy," she said,

dropping his hands. "Now come back in and get out of your feelings."

"Ah, you got jokes. I'm not in my feelings."

They never saw Ryan in the doorway as he watched the two of them holding hands. He knew that he had to step up his game. There was no girl who interested him as much as Shane Foster, and he was determined not to let her get away.

CHAPTER 5

Shane

Argh, I hate biology, and more than anything, I hate Mrs. Smith, Shane thought as she arrived at her third period class.

"Good morning, Shane," Mrs. Smith said with a huge smile on her face.

"Good morning," Shane responded, thoroughly confused. This woman was not one to speak, much less do it in a cheerful voice. Some of the other students looked at Shane curiously. They had occasionally witnessed an exchange of words between Shane and Mrs. Smith. They just didn't get along, but today she acted as if Shane was her favorite student.

Mrs. Smith already had their drill on the overhead when they walked into class. The state examination was coming up, so every teacher seemed to be focused on it. The only good thing about her class was the fact that Mrs. Smith only made them study for the test during the daily drill. After that, it was business as usual. All of it was a snoozefest for Shane. She knew science was really important. But she couldn't geek out. Science wasn't her thing.

Mrs. Smith made her usual stroll around the classroom, checking for homework. *Shoot, shoot, shoot,* Shane thought. *I forgot about my homework with all of the commotion at my house this weekend.*

"Shane, did you complete your homework?" Mrs. Smith asked her.

"No, Mrs. Smith. I had a really busy weekend. Honestly—"

Mrs. Smith stopped her where she was. She bent down to whisper in Shane's ear, which surprised the heck out of Shane. Their relationship had never been familiar enough for her to do that. If it had been Mrs. Monroe, then it would be different. This was Mrs. Smith, who was pegged as one of the scariest teachers in the school.

Shane could smell the activator Mrs. Smith used in her hair as she bent down. Mrs. Smith was one of the few people Shane knew who still wore a curl in her hair. In the eighties, many African American women wore curls. They were new and hip then. It made black hair curly and manageable. But it was very difficult to maintain. Most people had moved on to other styles.

In the 2000s, it was hard to find anyone who still used or sold the product. And then there was Mrs. Smith, who found the one person on the planet who could hook her up. "Shane, I saw you and your family on the news last night. I know it must have been a busy weekend for you. When is a good time for you to turn your assignment in to me?"

Huh, she's asking me? This is a first. "Well I could have it to you by the end of the day," Shane told her, still a bit confused as to what was happening.

"Tomorrow is fine, but don't make a habit out of it."

"Yes, ma'am." Shane thought she had died and landed in Bizarroland. *Too many chemicals in the biology room is driving this woman crazy.*

When Shane left from third period, it was time for lunch. She headed to her usual table to wait for Brandi and Marisa. Mrs. Smith had been so weird. She just had to share it with her besties. She spotted them at the salad bar and decided to join them. "Hey, you can't just cut in line," one of the girls at the end told her.

"Um, yeah, she kinda can," Brandi

responded as she made room for Shane to put together her salad.

"Thanks, B. How's y'all's day going?" she asked.

"Crazy slow. Wishing it was over," Brandi told her.

"I'm tired after your dad's announcement party last night. I just want to go to bed," Marisa told her.

"Yeah, well, my day was crazy," Shane told them. She told them how Mrs. Smith had treated her, and how she gave her an extra few hours on her homework. They were stunned.

"Girl, you know she's all political and stuff," Brandi told her.

"No, I had no clue."

"Yep, one time, when my mom went to vote, she was working the polls. She was all trying to get my mom to vote for some guy."

"Oh, now that explains it," Shane said as the lightbulb finally went off.

The girls sat down at the table with their salads and bottles of water. The new year had been an inspiration for all of them to start making healthier choices in their diets. They were trying to stick to it at school as well as at home.

While they were nibbling on their salads and chatting, the principal was making rounds in the cafeteria. "Good afternoon, ladies."

"Hi, Mrs. Montgomery," they all said.

"Well, you ladies must be exhausted. I caught a peek of you on the news last night. What time did your dad's announcement party end?" she asked Shane.

"I'm really not sure, Mrs. Montgomery. I just know I'm tired."

"Well, if you need to lie down in the nurse's office, be my guest. That goes for all of you. We are going to try to help you get through the election. It may be a tiring journey, but we will do what we can to help you."

"Thanks, Mrs. Montgomery," Shane said. "We really appreciate it."

"Oh, and, Shane, please tell your father that I think he will do our city proud. I live in Area 14, and he definitely has my vote."

By the end of the day, it was apparent to Shane that everybody in Port City knew or was about to find out that her father was running for office. Before he had decided to run, she really hadn't given much thought to city politics. There was a whole world going on in Port City that she had no idea about.

This day had been like no other day at PCH. Shane had a feeling there would be many more days like this. She knew change was coming for her family. She could feel it in the air.

CHAPTER 6

Marisa

The day of the Gap open call had finally arrived. Marisa had Trent bring her to the mall early that morning. She wanted to be one of the first people in line so she wouldn't look tired by the time she met with the casting agents. She was disappointed when she arrived and the line was out the door and growing by the second. The teenage hopefuls were plentiful, and the line had begun to wrap around the building.

"Do you want me to wait with you?"

Trent asked as he pulled his truck up to the end of the line.

"Nah, I'm good. I brought my tablet with me. I'm just going to download a new book or something. Don't worry about me. I'm in it for the long haul."

"Well, call me if you need anything. Hey," he stopped her before she could get out, "you lookin' right."

He made her blush. She climbed back in the huge Hummer truck and planted a kiss on his lips. It seemed that everybody was staring at her. It was making her feel awkward.

She definitely looked the part of a Gap model. She wore a pair of skinny jeans and a relaxed-fit white tee that hung off her shoulders, but in her bag she brought a spring outfit that would work perfectly with the brown riding boots she wore. And with the pair of polka dot flats she also had in her bag, she was ready for anything. She had a change of makeup, a change of clothing, snacks, and entertainment for herself. The only thing she hadn't brought was a chair. She never thought that she'd be so far back in the line.

Marisa definitely hadn't anticipated the amount of competition that would be there—people didn't stop adding to the line! The guys who showed up didn't bother her. It was the number of girls she would have to compete with that made her edgy. They were all so different.

What is the casting panel looking for? she wondered. She took out her tablet and began to study recent Gap ads. What was the look? What were they missing? And where could she fit?

She was jolted back to reality by a very attractive male who was helping with casting. "We need to get your picture," he informed her. His assistant took a Polaroid picture of her, and she was given an application to be completed before she made it to the front of the line.

It took two hours, but she finally made it to the door. She used her tablet to take a picture of herself in front of the door where the Gap casting sign was located. As soon as she posted her picture onto Friender, the Internet went nuts. Her friends immediately began to send notes of encouragement to her timeline.

Marisa saw a row of tables when she made it inside the door. A stylish young woman asked her for her application and the Polaroid picture that Marisa had been over-analyzing since it had been taken outside.

Once her paperwork was okayed, she was given a number and told to wait in one of the chairs that lined the wall.

Marisa sat down and took a deep breath. She had finally made it inside. *Now what happens next?*

Marisa took it all in. Where the Gap casting call was set up was the area the mall reserved for holiday events or promotions—like pictures with Santa or the Easter Bunny. Today there were five tables arranged in a semi-circle. At each table were two people. Marisa assumed one was a casting rep from the Gap and the other was their assistant.

One of the reps was constantly glancing over at her. Even while he was interviewing other potential models! He was making her nervous. *I really don't want to wind up at his table*, she thought.

"Hey." A young black girl with smoky gray eyes sat next to Marisa. Her naturally curly hair reminded her of Shane.

"Hey," Marisa said back to her.

"You nervous?" she asked.

"Not really. I have my moments, I guess, like at the entrance. The butterflies in my stomach started dancing."

"Girl, who you telling? Me too. I couldn't even sleep last night. I had to drive in from Bay City. We don't get many auditions where I live."

"Yeah, well, there aren't usually any in Port City either, but here we are."

"I'm Ella."

"Marisa. Nice to meet you. So have you modeled before?"

"My mom's had me modeling since I was two. I did a lot of ads for the local stores in Bay City, but nothing like Gap, ya know?"

"Wow. That's impressive. I've never been in any ads, not even locally."

"Is this your first audition?"

"Yeah."

"Well, welcome to the industry. You have the look, in my opinion. I'm sure you'll be around for a long time."

"Next, number two seventy-four!" the announcer called over the microphone.

"Well, that's me," Marisa told her new friend.

"Hey, are you on Friender?" Ella asked.

"Yeah, Marisa Maldonado. Don't forget to friend me."

"Doing it right now. Ella Pearson. Just in case it doesn't work."

"Good luck, Ella," Marisa said right before she was ushered beyond the ropes to where the casting reps sat. To her dismay, she was sent to the very rep who kept glancing her way. He made her uneasy. *Is it a coincidence that I'm at his table?* she wondered. She had to put any uncomfortable thoughts out of her mind in order to turn on her inner fabulousness. And she did, after all, *want* these people to like her appearance. She should be happy about the attention.

"You are Marisa Maldonado?" the female assistant sitting next to the casting rep asked her.

"Yes, ma'am. My friends call me Mari. I have three younger siblings. I'm a good student, and I'm driven. I'm young, but I know my worth," she said, feeling confident and secure. She wasn't sure where all of that came from, but it was as if she just knew how to read what they wanted, the wholesome, confident girl next door.

"So, why should we choose you out of all of the people in this room?" asked the man who had been looking at her. She shook off her nerves. She could do this. As she started to speak, she looked directly into his eyes.

"I am what Gap is missing. Most of the girls who look like they *might* be Hispanic in the ads make you wonder, is she Hispanic or white? With me, you'd know. When a young Hispanic girl flips through a magazine and sees an ad with my picture, I'll inspire her."

"You are not as tall as some of the other girls here. How tall are you?" the assistant asked, seeing if her confidence would waiver.

"I'm five seven, but what I lack in height, I make up for in every other way. I'm confident, secure, motivated, and ready," she assured the rep and his assistant.

The Gap representatives seemed to be impressed. She was given an orange ticket to move on to the next phase of casting. On the inside, she was doing back handsprings, but in front of the casting panel, she politely thanked them and went into the area designated for phase-two applicants. She posted on Friender that she was on to the next round of auditions, where she would compete with the best of the best. Everyone was excited for her.

When she saw Ella again, she was being ushered into the room as well, orange ticket in hand. "Well, we made it to the next round," Ella said excitedly. "Congrats on your first open call. It's huge to get past the first cut."

"Yeah, I'm excited. What time do you think we'll start round two? What are we going to do?"

"It kind of depends. No two auditions are ever the same." They waited for another thirty minutes before a panel of three casting reps arrived in the room.

A beautiful lady with a charming English accent greeted them. "Congratulations on making it this far in the process. First give yourselves a round of applause because one of you will be representing Texas in our next ad campaign.

"We're launching a state-to-state advertising campaign, and one of the first five states we'll focus on will be Texas. Today, we will have a small photo shoot. The five best pictures will compete with the other Texas hopefuls. Ultimately, we will choose one guy and one girl to represent your state.

"We should know who our models are in the next month or so. We will contact you via e-mail and phone. Any questions about round two? ... Great, then let's get started."

Marisa looked around the room at her competition. Everyone was absolutely gorgeous. They had weeded through the people who had come to the audition just because it was an open call and got down to the people with potential. *I am out of my league,* Marisa thought, looking around, but she quickly put the negativity out of her mind.

When it was her turn for her mini photo shoot, she nailed it. She knew her face and her angles, and she knew how to manipulate the camera. Her poses were deliberate but they looked effortless; her photos turned out versatile and inviting. The photographer loved her.

For the first pictures, she wore her jeans and off-the-shoulder white tee. As the shoot went on, she began to layer her clothing using the accessories she'd brought. First she added a scarf, and then she added a sweater for a nice fall look. The orange sweater contrasted beautifully with her naturally tanned skin.

When it was over, the photographer

thanked her and showed her the photos he thought were best. She had never been photographed by a professional before. The pictures were amazing. She couldn't believe that it was actually her. She *had* to win this job. She had never wanted anything more in her life.

CHAPTER 7

Brandi

*E*ver since Brandi returned home, things in her family had been on a better path. Her father blamed himself and his drug addiction for Brandi's willingness to connect to a stranger on the Internet. He thought it was the reason for her abduction. Brandi knew in her heart that he was right. If she was able to get the love she needed from him, then she probably never would have been so gullible.

What would my life be like if my father was never an addict? she wondered. She didn't know who she would be if he wasn't who he was. Now he was back and everything was supposed to be business as usual, but there was still uncertainty their home.

They all knew that their lives were much different than those of their friends and neighbors. They had to deal with the ugly face of addiction. Other families seemed to take it for granted how good they had it. Drugs abuse affected almost every decision that the Haywoods made.

Brandi could tell that her mother was struggling with her father's return. She was picking up double shifts to make ends meet. He was trying to play Mr. Mom, but he wasn't really good at it.

"You need to be out looking for a job, James. I want to spend more time with the girls. I can't continue to pull double shifts at the hospital. You have to pull your own weight around here."

"Dang, Cat, okay. Stop riding me all the time. I'm doing the best I can right now.

My homeboy is going to hook me up with a job at the plant. I just have to wait until they have something."

"You always looking for somebody to hook yo' black behind up. Get out there and get it on your own," she replied, disgusted at his lack of ambition.

Brandi's mother blamed herself for a lot of things. She had missed much of Brandi's formative years. And those times were so critical for young women. Mothers had to be vigilant with their daughters. You couldn't just tune out. But that's exactly what Mrs. Haywood felt she did.

She spent so many hours working, trying to keep her family afloat. Her remaining time was spent mopping up after her drug-addicted husband. When she wasn't worried about whether he was coming home or not, she was cleaning up vomit or trying to keep him hidden from his daughters when he was high as a kite.

She vowed that they were not going to

mess up Raven the way they had messed up Brandi. This round of rehab had better stick or she didn't know what would happen.

"I ain't looking for no hookups all the time. Oh, maybe Brian Foster knows if they're hiring at the city. I'ma talk to him tomorrow," Brandi's dad replied.

Catherine Haywood fell back into her thoughts. She was a bundle of nerves, but she wasn't going to show that side of herself to anyone. She didn't want to push her husband too hard. She didn't want to be the reason he relapsed. But inside, she was screaming at him and trying to make him understand that calling Brian was the same as waiting on a hookup from his "homeboy."

Surely he had heard of job boards and monster.com, but James Haywood had to be ushered into a position. He couldn't just find a job like a normal person. He had come from an upstanding family and had been a spoiled youngest son. Now his wife was left with a mess of a husband.

She knew that their girls needed their father, so she had to help him get through this. It was the only way they would meet the man that she had fallen in love with so many years ago in college. Before the drugs.

Time went by. She had finished school while he had smoked weed and dropped out. That should have been a red flag, but she was too in love to admit that he had a problem.

The arguments in the Haywood home weren't aggressive. There were no broken plates or holes in the wall; however, they were still far from a perfect household. Brandi knew her parents were on the right track. There had been real improvement. But she longed for the family environment that Shane or Marisa had. Their homes seemed "perfectly flawed."

All families had their problems, she knew that. Her family's problems seemed extraordinary. There was never anything ordinary about being an addict. Not only did the individual suffer, but the family suffered too. Brandi had heard that addiction was a selfish disease, and the truth of that was now becoming clear to her.

When she was younger, she wasn't able to understand her mother, but now she was beginning to. Catherine Haywood was alone too. Brandi and Raven had been fatherless during the really rough times, but their mother was husbandless. Husbandless with a husband was one of the worst things a woman could be. Brandi was determined to not follow in her mother's footsteps on that one.

Her boyfriend, Bryce, was obviously not the caring and consoling individual that Brandi had dreamed he would be. His mother's addiction left him just as scarred as she was feeling. She couldn't get the little stunt he pulled at school out of her mind. It was a red flag.

He was volatile. She couldn't keep on excusing his behavior. It was always the same thing. After he got angry, he cozied up to her to make it all better. She fell for it every time. It wasn't until she was alone in her room that she could admit to herself what a fool she was. She was more like her mother than she realized. Otherwise she would have dumped him the first time he lost his cool.

One thing she had learned from her kidnapping was to trust her instincts, and they were telling her to get out while the getting was good.

CHAPTER 8

Dodging Cupid's Arrow

I hate Valentine's Day!" Shane announced as she joined her two best friends at their lockers. "It's so cheesy."

"You just mad 'cause you're not in love right now," Brandi told her.

"This is my favorite holiday," Marisa said, smiling. "Especially since I have Trent." Marisa did a quick twirl in the hallway, her hands covering her heart.

"Yeah, well, I don't want any part of

the dance this weekend. Well, I'm going to be there, but just to get some pics for the newspaper."

"Get one of those geeky people you hang around on yearbook committee to do that so you and Ashton can roll with me and Trent. He asked if you had a date yet," Marisa said, warning her that he was interested in taking her.

"He called hinting at the fact that he wanted to take me, but Ryan asked too. I'm not ready to go to the Valentine's dance with either one of them. It seems like it could be taken the wrong way."

"Only Shane would have two dates for the dance and choose neither," Brandi retorted. "You want me to see if Bryce has a friend or something, then it won't be so major of a decision?"

"I guess y'all not understanding that I don't want to go at all—with anybody."

They exited the building to look for Robin. It was Tuesday night. There was a basketball home game. The girls were headed to catch a bite to eat at Jerry's before the game. The Port City High Wildcats were playing the Texas City High Tigers, whose team was having a great year. The anticipation for the game had been building on Friender, where both teams were going back-and-forth, debating who would be the ultimate winner.

"Did you talk to Trent today?" Shane asked Marisa. "Is he ready for the game tonight? The Tigers have been talking so much trash. We have to win."

"Girl, Trent is always ready. My man is the truth."

They heard giggles behind them as Marisa made her declaration. It was Ashley Rivera again. Marisa had attempted to be friends with Ashley after years of beefing, but when she caught her shamelessly flirting with Trent, she knew that she had to get her out of her life for good. Now here she was trying to cause problems where no problems existed. Marisa was deter-mined not to fall for it again.

"What you laughing at?" Brandi asked, welcoming one of Ashley's little friends to jump fly.

"Nothing, we were just saying the same thing, and we thought it was ironic," Ashley told them.

"And what would that be?" Shane asked defensively.

"I was just saying that Trent was the truth too. If I wasn't dating Dalton, it'd be a different story."

"Are you serious right now, Ashley?" Marisa asked, taking the bait. "I'm the one who hooked you up with Dalton, and he don't even want yo' trifling behind." Dalton and Ashley had double dated with Marisa and Trent, but he just wasn't into her and Marisa knew it. Dalton Broussard, power forward for PCH, could have any girl he wanted, and Ashley wasn't it.

"If he didn't want me, then why would

he be taking me to the Valentine's dance this weekend?" she asked sarcastically.

"Maybe because he wants somebody who's down to be trampish ... like you," Shane said calmly and walked away from the mayhem to flag down her sister.

"Oh no you didn't! I don't get down like that!" Ashley shouted. She ran after Shane, getting in her face.

"Yeah, right, Ashley. That's not what Dalton told me last year when he was all up on me and every other girl at this school. Everybody knows what Dalton is about. And quite frankly," Shane said, lowering her voice to a whisper and leaning toward Ashley, "they all know what you're about too."

Ashley's arm flew back in an attempt to slap Shane across the face, but Shane saw it coming and had her by the throat before she could make contact. Ashley's face turned as red as the Valentine hearts that decorated the fence that Shane threw her up against. "You ain't 'bout that life, Ashley. I've been wishing you would step to me. Don't make that mistake again," she warned her as Ashley tried to regain her composure.

"Have fun at the dance," Marisa shouted back, laughing as they jumped in the car with Robin and Aiden.

"You did Ashley so wrong," Brandi said, laughing as they got in the car.

"I know, but she was about to slap me. What else could I do?" Shane asked innocently.

"Oh no, what happened?" Robin asked.

Brandi gave her the whole story in her usual animated way. They laughed at Ashley and her weak little crew that did nothing to come to her aid. "I can't believe they just stood there," Robin said.

"They saw the looks our faces and opted out of that one," Brandi told them. "It would have been three on three, and they knew we'd had enough of Ashley's mouth. I don't think they were willing to take the hit for her on that one."

"I was so ready, and you know I'm not a fighter, but Ashley is just a disrespectful little witch. I tried to be nice to her. I really did," Marisa told them.

"You did," Shane said to her.

"That's a couple of days of your life you can never get back. What a waste," Brandi told her.

They arrived at Jerry's and ordered their food. Brandi had to be back at school with the cheerleaders in one hour, so they had to eat quickly.

"Hey, let me hold Aiden while y'all eat," Marisa told them.

"Here we go again. That Gap audition better not have you starving yourself."

"No, I'm not, but my appetite is slim to none. I just want to hear back from them so badly. They did send an e-mail telling me that I was one of the finalists," she said as a smile crept to her face.

"What?! You didn't even tell us! Does Trent know?" They all began talking at once.

"I haven't told anybody," she admitted. "I didn't want to jinx it, but I couldn't hold it in any longer."

"That's so awesome, Mari," Robin told her, giving her a huge hug as they squeezed Aiden between them.

As soon as they were done stuffing their faces, they headed to the game. Brandi went to the gym to meet the cheerleaders, and Shane went to work taking pictures. Marisa and Robin found a seat right behind the basketball team, but close enough to the aisle so that Robin could get to the restroom if Aiden had to be changed.

Aiden's father, Gavin, joined the girls shortly after they sat down to help Robin with the baby. Even though they had both graduated the year before, they loved attending the games. Basketball was huge in Port City and gained support from almost half the community.

When the Wildcats hit the court, the crowd went crazy. The Tigers team hadn't come alone, though. Many of their fans had come to support them, but there was nothing like home-court advantage.

Trent threw his favorite towel to Marisa as he passed by her and Robin. It was his way of letting her know that he was thinking about her.

Unfortunately, the Wildcat's entrance would turn out to be the most exciting part of the evening. By halftime, everybody realized it was going to be a snoozefest.

The Tigers had gained a lot of clout in their area, but they were no match for the Wildcats' zone defense or for Trent's fast breaks. After Trent's second slam dunk, he was benched by Coach Mac along with Ashton and Dalton. The second string players had taken their place on the court, and that left the first string to chill until the game was over.

The Tigers had talked a lot of noise on Friender, but when they came to PCH, it was a blowout. The Tigers' fans started to leave before the game was over. By the end of fourth quarter, the only people left in the stands were Wildcats' fans.

The PCH fans probably would have left too if it wasn't Valentine's week. Rumor had it that many players on the basketball team were still without dates. The girls flocked to the court when the game was over.

Shane busied herself with her photography in the bleachers. It took her by surprise when her lens fell on Ashton talking to one of Ashley's friends, Courtney Bernard. Courtney was one of the girls who was with Ashley when Shane almost beat her down. *Nice try,* Shane thought.

She slowly relocated to the court area where she could get a better look at what was going on. Ashton put his number in Courtney's phone, and she added her number to his. Shane knew that something was going on; she just had to find out what.

As soon as Courtney walked away, she zoomed her camera in on Ashton as he tied his shoes on the bench. "That's the best look you got for me, Ashton?" she hollered.

"Hey, there she is! You get some good pics of me with that thing?" he asked.

"You wanna see?" she asked, handing him the camera. He scrolled through the pictures, but the only ones on there were of him and Courtney. "Y'all lookin' all couple cute and stuff," she joked.

He smacked his lips. "Nah, it ain't like that. We just going to the Valentine's dance together."

"You're taking Courtney," she paused, "to the Valentine's dance? C'mon."

"Don't act like that. You know I wanna go with you. You're *making* me go with her."

"I can't make you do anything, fool."

"Tell me you'll come with me and she's history."

Out of the corner of her eye, she saw Ryan as he entered the gym. He looked like he was looking for somebody. *Dang. I know he's looking for me,* she thought. *And he's going to see me talking to Ashton.*

He raised himself on his toes and gestured to someone. He was talking to the only white girl on the cheerleading squad. She ran over to talk to him, pompoms shaking. Shane felt sick to her stomach. *What the heck is going on today?*

"Shane?" Ashton asked, confused. "Earth to Shane," he said, following her gaze to Ryan. "Oh, it's good, Shane. You go see nerdy boy and hit me later."

"Wait, what? Ashton?" She tried to get

his attention, but he was gone. "Shoot," she said to herself and went to find her friends.

The day of the Valentine's dance was rainy and cold. It was by no means weather to be out in little dresses trying to look cute. Shane was happy she had opted out of going to the dance. She put on warm-ups, a cozy green sweater, her brown Uggs, and a cute polka-dot knit hat that she slipped over her unruly mane.

She looked like a true photographer as she slipped through the cafeteria door. There were only two other students there to take pictures. They divided the work into sections and prepared for the task of completing this week's newspaper.

When Ashley, Dalton, Courtney, and Ashton walked into the dance, they stood in her section right by the refreshment table. She was supposed to be getting pictures of them, but she just couldn't do it. She would never immortalize that little group.

She was so relieved when she saw Brandi walk through the door. She had to admit her girl was looking cute. Her thick hair was pulled into a tight bun on the top of her head, and her makeup was flawless. Brandi's skin looked as smooth as melted chocolate. Bryce was close behind her with his hand on the small of her back. *He's so controlling. I hate that loser,* Shane thought as she walked over to greet her friend. "You look hot, B," she said, giving her a hug. "Let me get some pics of y'all."

Brandi and Bryce posed for the camera, looking like the cutest couple ever. Brandi's dark chocolate skin and his caramel color blended together perfectly. *Too bad looks ain't everything,* Shane thought.

"Hold up, hold up! My girl done entered the building. It's America's Next Top Model," Shane announced, snapping Marisa's picture as she walked through the door. Marisa halfheartedly protested the attention from her BFF. Shane looked at the shots she took of Marisa in her camera. "Girl, you've been studying your angles. You make me look like a pro."

"You know baby got it like that," Trent said, kissing her on the lips. She wiped the residue of lip gloss off his lips. Anybody looking could see they were in love. They made such a ruckus at the entrance of the cafeteria that people were starting to turn and stare. Ashton came rushing over to talk to Trent. "Big T! My dude."

"Ash! Where my ninja at?"

"Them girls have Dalton on a tight leash. They mad that we wanted to come over here, something about Shane." He turned his attention to her. "What you do to Ashley the other day?"

"I don't know what you talking about," she lied.

"She choked her!" Brandi jumped in.

"Is that why Courtney asked me to

come to the dance? To piss you off? I feel used, but I'ma let her use me all night," he jokingly said, dancing to the music.

"You working or playing?" She heard a rough voice behind her. She knew it was Ryan.

She turned around and stepped back so that he could see her clothes. Even in her Uggs and warm-ups, she was confident. All the girls around her were made up like little porcelain dolls, and there she stood, casual and comfortable. Most girls would have cared, but not Shane.

"Don't I look like I'm working?" she asked him.

"Looks can be deceiving," he told her, still holding tightly to his date's hand. "You're not going to get our picture?" he asked Shane with a smile creeping to his lips. He knew he was messing with her.

"Boy, I'm not taking your picture with another female. Stop," she said boldly.

"Yo, let me go tend to my date. I'ma

catch y'all later, T," Ashton said, dapping up his best friend and rolling his eyes at Shane, who was flirting in his face.

"I'm going to the ladies' room, Ryan. I'll be right back," Ryan's date told him.

"I'll be right here, Kelsey." When she walked away, he turned to Shane. "Why did you do that?"

"What? I didn't do anything." Shane was having more fun at the dance messing with Ashton and Ryan than if she had actually gone to the dance with either of them. Ryan just shook his head at her. He had never met anyone like her before. She was so unpredictable.

When Ryan walked away, Marisa scolded her, "You need to stop picking on Ashton. I know he's a clown most of the time, but he really likes you."

"I was just about to say the same thing about Ryan. I feel sorry for the guy," Brandi told her. "And even worse for Kelsey. That's my girl too."

"They'll be all right. They shouldn't have come with dates."

"Girl, can't nobody wait around for yo' yellow behind," Brandi told her. "What did you expect?"

"You are a trip, Shane Foster. I'm glad we are friends 'cause you really do have problems," Marisa told her.

CHAPTER 9

Shane

Screaming and yelling were not a common thing in the Fosters' home. Most of the time there was peace and harmony. If there was a disagreement between the Fosters, they were usually able to discuss it in a calm manner. But today was different. Shane could hear her mother's voice from upstairs. She opened her bedroom door at the same time as Robin. They looked at each other. Both shrugged their shoulders. Aiden was fast asleep, so the two of them tip-toed to the top of the staircase to eavesdrop.

"Who is she, Brian? When did it happen?"

"It was a long time ago. You'd just had Shane, and—"

"So when I was at home with our newborn, you were with ... what's her name again? How could you, Brian?" They could hear the pain in their mother's voice. She was hurting. "And now she's saying there's a child. Come on! Where was I when all of this was going on? Is it possible that the baby's yours? Tell me the truth."

"Kim, that girl is not my daughter."

"How can you know for sure?"

"I just know. I used protection."

They could hear a slap as it landed on their father's face. Then footsteps as her heels hit the hardwood floors. Her pace was quick and deliberate. "I never thought that I would be having this conversation with you. Brian Foster, former Navy Seal, always controlled, always following the rules! You disgust me!" their mother yelled.

"Kimberly, don't leave!" their father screamed at her as her keys jingled in her hands.

"Oh, I'm leaving before I do or say something that we will both regret."

She slammed the front door so hard that it shook the entire house. Her truck screeched as she backed out of the driveway. She sounded like she was escaping, not just leaving for a while. They could see their father as he looked out the window as her car sped away. When he turned away from the window, his eyes locked on his two daughters, who were still sitting on the top step. They both looked like little girls again, and he was embarrassed by what they had overheard.

The slamming door had woken Aiden, and his cry cut through the silence. The Fosters each needed space to digest what had happened. The air in their house had begun to close in on them, and they all went opposite directions.

Later that evening, Shane and Robin sat together trying to make sense of the conversation they had overheard.

"He said that it was a long time ago," Shane said, taking up for her father.

"Are you serious, Shane? I can't imagine Gavin telling me that he had been cheating on me right after I had Aiden. That's not cool."

"Yeah, well ..." She didn't know what to say. "Do you think Mom will stay with him?"

"I don't know. She hasn't come home yet," Robin said, looking out the window as if that would bring their mother home. "She probably needs time to cool off."

Shane stayed in Robin's room until they heard their mother's truck. "She's here," Robin warned Shane. They were bracing themselves for round two, but they didn't hear a sound. Their parents locked themselves in their bedroom and didn't come out.

Early the next morning, they were called downstairs for a family meeting. "Girls, your father has something he wants to talk to you about."

Brian Foster cleared his throat. This was his toughest audience, and he knew it. He wanted his daughters to respect him. He wanted to be *worthy* of their respect. He wanted to set a good example. "There's going to be an article in the newspaper. It's going to say things about me. Some of them are true, and some of them are not." They could tell he was struggling.

"It's going to be in the newspaper? The *Port City Tribune*?" Shane asked, shocked that their family's business was going to be out there for everyone to see.

"No, it's actually going to appear in the *Messenger* this week, but who knows where it could go after that. The *Port City*

Tribune may pick it up later. They have a tendency to do that."

"Let him finish, Shane. I want to hear what Dad has to say."

He cleared his throat again. "Okay, well, they interviewed a lady who I used to work with. During the interview, this woman claimed that we'd had an affair."

"Did you?" Robin asked abruptly.

"We had a relationship, yes, but it was a long time ago. Your mother and I—"

"And what about this child we heard you and Mom yelling about? Do we have a half-sister, Dad?" Shane asked her father. Everyone was surprised that she was being so blunt.

He felt very uncomfortable talking to his daughters about such a personal matter. He was humiliated and embarrassed. But his daughters were getting older. He had to prepare them for the rumors and the fallout that was sure to come.

He looked at his wife, who had her arms folded, shutting him and his words out. "We're going to have to do a DNA test. She never told me about a baby back then, so I really don't think that the girl is my daughter."

"Wow," Robin said, disgusted. "Everything's different. Everything!"

"You really did this, Daddy? You really cheated on Mom right after she had me?" Shane asked him, crushed.

"I did." His body slumped, and he looked as though he would cry. "Your mother and I ... we have a great relationship. But back then ... I was having a rough time. You'll see what I mean one day. I made a mistake."

"A rough time for *you*? You have no idea what it's like having a baby. I'm sure it was a rough time for her too. I hope that my husband is better than you are. I hope I never have to 'see what you mean,'" Robin snapped.

As much as Mrs. Foster wanted to let the girls badger their father, she knew that she had to step in. "Girls, I made mistakes during that time too. I may not have cheated, but I could have done some things differently."

"You were postpartum, Mom, you'd had a baby. Don't you dare take up for him." Robin's voice was getting louder and louder.

"So we have to be in public and put on a united front, don't we? What are we supposed to say?" Shane asked him, but she didn't really want an answer. "You said that you wouldn't let this election hurt us, Dad. Well, guess what? It's hurting us," she screamed at him as the tears she'd tried to hold back burned her cheeks.

"You hurt me, Dad. *You* did, not the election. You are not the man I thought you were." Robin's words pierced his heart as he sat at the kitchen table.

"Girls, that's enough," their mother told them. "Normally, parents wouldn't have to be so candid about their relationship, but we didn't want you to find out from the newspaper."

"We don't even read the stupid *Messenger*," Robin told them.

"But you know people who do," their father said without looking at his daughters. "And plus, we can put all of this behind us when I win. Surely you both will be happy about that."

"If you win, Dad. We could go through all of this and you could lose. Have you even considered that?" Robin asked. He didn't have an answer for her. "You know, I feel like we already lost, but we lost something worse than this election. We lost our family."

The Fosters were exhausted. It was only ten in the morning, but they were all feeling frazzled and tired. Shane and Robin were both hurt and wanted to spend some time away from home.

They grabbed their keys, their laptops, and Aiden. They went to the one place where they could find some peace: Starbucks. A good coffee drink could make everything a little more bearable.

CHAPTER 10

Marisa

Marisa Maldonado, please," the unfamiliar voice said.

"This is Marisa."

"This is Stormy calling from Gap. Do you have a minute?"

"Yes, ma'am, I do." Marisa could feel her heart beating rapidly. She sat down on her bed, anxiously waiting for Stormy to respond.

She had already prepared herself to hear the words and had practiced her reaction. *It's okay. I'll just have to try again next time, but thank you so much for considering me.* She didn't want to get her hopes up. She knew that this open call was a shot in the dark.

"Well, I have news for you about the casting call. Are you sitting down?"

Just say it already, she thought.

"Gap has decided to use you in the new fall ad campaign. The shoot will be done in Houston." Marisa began to dance in her room like a maniac. She was quiet enough; Stormy couldn't hear it, but she was dancing. "Will that be a problem?"

"No," she said, trying to catch her breath.

"Are you okay?" Stormy asked, concerned by the change in Marisa's voice.

"Oh, I'm better than okay. I'm elated, excited, and nervous all at the same time."

Stormy laughed. "Well, good. Keep that energy and bring it with you on Monday. And Marisa ... welcome to Gap."

Marisa did laps around the house. She went through the living room where her sisters were watching television, past the kitchen where her mom was making her father's favorite soup, and into Romero's room where he was working hard to beat his best friend Sam on his Xbox. She could hear the concern in their voices as she screamed and yelled as loud as she could.

"I got it. I did it. I got it. I did it," she kept chanting over and over.

They didn't know what she was talking about. "Something's wrong with her," she heard her sisters say.

"Slow down, *mi hija*," her mother's voice faded out as she was on to the next room.

"Something is *so* wrong with your sister, dude," she could hear Samuel warning Romero.

She collapsed on the living room floor. They all gathered to find out what was going on. "I did it. I landed the Gap ad," she said breathlessly.

Her little sisters, Isi and Nadia, began to jump up and down. It took her mom a moment for the news to sink in. They all needed something positive to happen, and this was it. Her mother's hands moved slowly to her mouth as the tears fell from her eyes.

She had always encouraged Marisa in her modeling, but she thought it was an improbable dream. She would have preferred if she'd gone to math or science camp. But she knew that this was a dream come true for her daughter, and she had done it on her own.

Romero explained to Samuel what was going on, and he was thoroughly impressed. "Cool, Mari! Can I get your autograph? I know a real live model."

Marisa was spent from her sprint around the house, but she pulled herself together and called her girls. Once all calls had been joined, she just began to scream. "I got it! I got the Gap ad!" Shane and Brandi shouted congratulations to Marisa. They were excited for their friend.

By the time her dad got home, she had simmered down. She was able to calmly explain what happened and give him all the details. He was concerned about his daughter entering that world at such a young age, but their family needed the extra income, and Marisa swore she would use it to help them get out of the hole they were in.

"I'm proud of you, mi hija," her father told her, kissing her gently on the forehead.

On the Friday before the shoot, Mrs. Maldonado reminded Marisa to pick up her assignments from her teachers for the following Monday.

The Maldonados were determined that Marisa would not get behind in her schoolwork just because she was modeling. Marisa promised them that she would get her schoolwork done.

All weekend long, she prepared for her first photo shoot. She was at the mirror practicing her angles. She drank water constantly so her skin could stay well-hydrated, and she ate fruit to illuminate her natural skin tone. The last thing she wanted was to look dehydrated and malnourished.

Her call time was eight that Monday morning, which meant that she had to be up by five. If the Maldonados could have afforded it, Marisa and her mom would have driven to Houston on Sunday and relaxed in a hotel for the early-morning shoot on Monday. But that was out of the question. Luckily, they wanted her to come with clean hair and face, which meant no makeup or hair care was needed, just wash and go.

As soon as she walked into the studio, she was introduced to the hair and makeup team that would be working with her. They started with hair first. Marisa was instructed to come to the shoot with freshly washed hair that had no product added after washing. The hair team spritzed her hair with water, then gave her a blowout. Next came oversized rollers, which set while her makeup was applied.

The makeup artist was a twentyish Asian girl with numerous tattoos. She had a few strategically placed piercings that Marisa thought were really cool. Marisa realized she was a little intimidated by this interesting young woman. She seemed unapproachable, so Marisa just sat quietly until the makeup artist broke the silence.

"Is this your first shoot?" she asked.

Marisa looked up. After what seemed like thirty minutes of silence, she was caught off guard. "Yes," she said shyly. "Can you tell?"

The makeup artist laughed. "Yeah, but it's cool. We all start somewhere. I'm Alexis."

"I'm Marisa, but call me Mari."

"Well, Mari, I think that you'll do just

fine. You have a good look, and I've seen a lot of looks."

"Thanks," Marisa told her and went back to studying the assignment for her English class. The vocabulary words that she had to learn seemed to be the easiest thing to study while having to meet Alexis's demands.

"Close your eyes. Tilt your head. Look to the right."

Marisa was constantly losing her focus. What made her think she could concentrate when everyone around her was so busy? Not only that, she was ordered to tilt her head up, down, right, and left every few minutes.

She had never understood how long it took to properly apply makeup for a photo shoot. She gasped when Alexis pulled out an airbrush.

"Hey," Alexis said. "Don't be nervous. This is a really cool tool. All your photos will be indoors, so I don't want you to look washed out. Your skin will be a touch darker than you're used to. But don't freak out. The photos will be fab."

"I never thought I'd need ... is something wrong with me?" Marisa asked nervously.

"Heck no! You are gorgeous. This will just apply a fine mist of makeup. The flash won't bounce the light off your skin. And if you get hot? The color won't change. My work never smudges," Alexis said proudly.

"Who knew?" Mari smiled. "This is beyond sweet!"

And with that, Marisa decided to put her schoolwork aside. There was no way she could pull off the photo shoot that would launch her career *and* do her English assignment at the same time.

Her hair was styled by a guy named Marco, who seemed to know how to work magic. She had never seen her hair look this good. He was pleased that she was pleased. It had taken three hours to do hair and makeup alone.

By the time she arrived at wardrobe, she felt like she needed a nap. She was waiting patiently when her mother showed up, asking if she had eaten anything. She hadn't even thought of food in the past three hours. She was more focused on completing the shoot and living up to expectations.

She declined her mother's offer to eat and went into wardrobe, where they fussed over the perfect look for the shot. In the end, she wore a pair of jeans that tightly hugged her body, a plaid shirt, brown boots, and a stylish scarf.

It was amazing. There were so many people running around trying to perfect this shoot. But Marisa felt like a bystander until she got in front of the camera and realized that all this fuss was for her. She was the star of the day, and it felt like it. The experience was surreal.

As the photographer gave her directions, she did her best to give him what she thought he was looking for. "Wonderful, don't lose your neck. Extend, extend. Throw the leaves into the air. Look toward the light. Look happy. Good, good." She felt like a contortionist. "Now let's take a break," he said after an hour of shooting.

"You did great, mi hija," her mother said, handing her a bottle of water.

When she returned to the set, there was a young male model there to shoot with her. He was possibly the cutest white boy Marisa had ever laid eyes on. His etched face gave him a superhero appearance. He was absolutely gorgeous.

Marisa could feel her heart thumping as he introduced himself. His wardrobe mirrored hers. The navy blue sweater he wore picked up the colors in her flannel. They added a navy blue infinity scarf to Marisa's wardrobe plus a cute hat with a flower. The two made an adorable couple.

"Here we go, people!" the photographer's assistant yelled.

The sound of the fan whirling, let the models know that it was game on. The scene was set for them. "It's a regular autumn day. The leaves have begun to fall. It's breezy. The two of you are strolling through the park. You stop to take in the moment and enjoy a quiet Sunday afternoon together. Whatever you do, don't forget you're here for the clothing. Let's go."

Marisa's partner turned it up. As he posed, she slinked into the crevasses of his body. They looked as though they were having fun. They looked like a real couple who just fit. The laughter they shared was realistic. He was a cool kid. He picked up the leaves from the ground and playfully let them fall like rain on her head. She smiled up at him as the leaves danced in the air. The shoot was magical. They were young and fresh, just what the photographer said Gap was looking for.

When they finished that portion of the shoot, Marisa was approached by one of the ladies who had been observing them. "Hey, that was great. I really enjoyed watching your shoot today."

"Oh, thanks," Marisa said, appreciating the compliment, but exhausted from the long day. It was already four in the afternoon, and they still had to drive all the way back to Port City.

Her mother had already started gathering their things.

"I'm Marcie Miller," she said, handing Marisa her business card, which read Miller & Miller Modeling Inc. "I wanted to talk to you about representation. At Miller and Miller, we are always looking for fresh faces, and you definitely have that. Do you already have an agent?"

Marisa had never thought about having an agent. She was just reacting to what was going on around her. Her plan had only gone as far as beating out the competition at the casting call and booking the job.

Her mother was just a couple of steps away, listening to the whole conversation. She stepped in just in time. "I'm Marisa's mother, Lupe. Do you mind if I have one of your cards? We can give you a call later this week."

Marisa was so thankful that her mother was able to speak English with confidence. She couldn't imagine if she had to navigate through this new world of modeling alone.

"That's a wonderful idea," Marcie said. "Just know that what I saw today shows some really raw talent. I believe that Marisa can go far. Why don't you do some research on our agency and then give me a call." She turned to Marisa. "It was nice to meet you. We look forward to working with you."

After Marcie left the Maldonados alone, her mother turned to her with tears in her eyes. "You made me so proud today, mi hija. And now we can check out this agent and see if she's any good. I know your father wants to know all the details. I can't wait to tell him. This is such a wonderful opportunity for you, but I want you to remember, school comes first." She looked stern. "If your grades drop, no more modeling until you can prove you can handle it."

Marisa knew her mother was right. She would do her best with her grades. But what she was really fixated on was her glamorous new career. She felt like her life was just beginning. Maybe she would make it to Paris and Milan someday. She felt like her life was just beginning.

CHAPTER 11

Brandi

"Get dressed," Brandi's mother said, pulling the covers off her daughter. "It's almost eleven."

"Whaaat, Mom? It's spring break! All I want to do is sleep these ten days away."

"Negative. Raven," her mother yelled. "We have good news for you girls. We are going to that new restaurant For Starters to celebrate because Daddy got a job yesterday at the plant."

"What? Are you serious?" Brandi asked, excited for her father.

Raven started singing and dancing.

"New clothes, new clothes. Mama, can I get the new pink Js?" she asked.

"Can you stop spending your father's checks before he gets them?" her mother asked playfully.

"Mom, that's cool and all, but I was going to meet up with Bryce this afternoon. Is it okay if he joins us?"

Her mom was skeptical about her relationship with Bryce, and Brandi knew it. "Well, this is more for family, B," she said. "But I guess it's okay." She wanted them to be in a celebratory mood, which meant that she would have to put up with Bryce.

"Cool, Mom!" Brandi said excitedly. "Thank you, thank you, thank you. I'm going to call Bryce."

After Brandi called Bryce, she left to get ready for their afternoon lunch. It was the first time that her family was going to spend time with him in an intimate setting. She just prayed they would warm up to him, even while that voice in her head told her to back off. There had been red flags all over the place, but Brandi was hoping she was wrong. Maybe Bryce could pull it together.

In the car, Brandi could hear her parents discussing an article that had appeared in the newspaper; she knew it had to be about Mr. Foster.

"I just can't believe Brian is the cheating type. He's so buttoned-up," her mother said.

"I just hope that the child is not his. I'm thinking Kim would leave my boy if that was the case. You see, baby, everybody makes mistakes. At least you don't have to worry about me cheating on you," her father responded.

"I better not. We already have too much going on as it is."

They pulled up to Bryce's house to pick him up. It was a modest home that he shared with his grandmother, who waved at them from the porch.

"Go in the house, Momo," he yelled at her. He seemed to be in an awful mood. It was in obvious contrast to the playful, upbeat vibe that was going on in the Haywoods' car.

"How are you, Bryce?" Mrs. Haywood asked.

"I'm good. Thanks for letting me roll with y'all."

"Thanks for rolling with us," her father said, noticing how rough Bryce was around the edges. He was not the kind of boy he wanted his daughter dating. He was bettering himself so that his daughters would make better choices. And Bryce had an air of defiance and smugness about him that didn't sit well with Mr. Haywood.

He knew he hadn't been the best role model for his oldest daughter. But he hadn't realized until his last stint in rehab how much his choices influenced her actions. While Bryce was not like him, he was truly a damaged boy. And he did not want his daughters ending up with men who could harm them emotionally or physically. Men like him.

Bryce sat back listening to the family interaction. When he first met Brandi, their lives seemed similar. Even more so when they started dating. Both of their parents were battling drug addiction. Brandi basically had no father. Now it had all changed for her, and he was feeling alone. He scrolled through his phone and noticed that Matthew Kincade, Brandi's ex-boyfriend, had posted on her Friender timeline.

"What's this?" he asked, showing Brandi the Friender page on his phone.

"I guess that's a post on my timeline. What?" she whispered so that her parents wouldn't hear them.

"What's Matthew doing asking you what's up?" he hissed.

"You two okay back there?" her mother asked.

"Yeah, we good," he said and turned to look out the window.

When they arrived at the restaurant, Bryce looked at the sign: For Starters, A Tapas Experience. "What's *tapas*?" Bryce asked, his face contorting like there was a foul odor in the air.

"It's when a restaurant focuses on appetizers instead of large meals," Mrs. Haywood explained. "It's one way of tasting a variety of food in one place. It's new, so we thought we'd try it."

"Well, I don't think I'm going to like it."

"There's a McDonald's down the street if that's better for you," Mr. Haywood told him, annoyed by his negativity. There was no way he was about to let this angry little punk ruin their mood. Bryce shot him a look like he was tempted to say something smart, but by the expression on Mr. Haywood's face, he thought better of it.

"I'm good," he replied, cowering under Mr. Haywood's gaze.

The rest of the time at the restaurant, the Haywoods tried to ignore Bryce and his negative comments. He was a hurt little kid with a chip on his shoulder, which was a horrible combination.

They dined on tuna tartar, fried macaroni and cheese, boudin balls, crab-stuffed peppers, and jalapeño poppers. The fresh strawberry lemonade really quenched their thirst. The Haywood family hadn't had an afternoon lunch that tasted this good in a long time. After Bryce tasted the food at For Starters, his attitude even began to improve. A little.

As soon as they left the restaurant, they headed to the park to feed the ducks and enjoy the beautiful spring day.

Mr. Haywood took Raven to the swings and gave her a push to get her going. Then he stood back and watched her happy face.

Their mother sat down on one of the benches. It was a joy for her to be watching her family having a good time. As Brandi and Bryce strolled around the duck pond, Bryce's attitude suddenly shifted.

"What's wrong?" Brandi asked. When he didn't respond, she followed his gaze. She saw Matthew Kincade coming their way.

"Hey, B! What are y'all doing here? I just now noticed your moms over there on the bench."

"Hey, Mattie," she said nervously, knowing Bryce was probably still mad about the Friender post. "Did Dad see you? He just asked about you the other day."

"Aw, man. I didn't know that your dad was back in town. That's great! Where's Raven?

"Um, I hate to break up y'all's little reunion, but I ain't havin' none of this. You just gonna disrespect me like I ain't even standin' here?"

Brandi had seen this change in Bryce's personality before, and she knew that he was about to get irate. Again the red-flag alert went off in her head. Trying to avoid a scene, she said, "Baby, I'm sorry. I wasn't trying to disrespect you." She looked at Matthew apologetically with her eyes.

"Man, you ain't 'bout to sit here talking to me like I'm a chump or somethin'," Bryce hissed between clenched teeth. "I can see what's goin' on here, and I'm not down with it at all."

Brandi was losing her patience and becoming more embarrassed. "You trippin', Bryce. You supposed to know I'm your ride or die, but you treating me like I'm out here running around on you just because I spoke to Matthew. Of course he knows my family. We were together for two years."

"Man, forget this," Bryce said, pushing Brandi. She lost her balance and fell to the ground. When her father saw her fall, he ran from the playground area toward Bryce. Before he could get there, Matthew was in Bryce's face.

"Man, what's wrong with you? Don't you know everything she's been through? Now here you come, making her situation worse."

"Dog, you better back up off me!" Bryce yelled at him.

"Nah, you wanna put your hands on her. Put your hands on me, pretty boy." Matthew jumped at him like he was going to slap him in the face. Bryce flinched. "That's what I thought. You a scared li'l punk."

"I ain't scared of nobody," Bryce said, taking his jacket off. Before the jacket hit the ground, Matthew punched him in the nose, sending blood flying through the air.

"Mattie!" Brandi yelled. "Don't," she begged him. She knew that Matthew would hurt Bryce. Even though he had pushed her, she didn't want it to get violent.

"I'm sorry, B. I was just trying to speak to you and the fam."

Mr. Haywood, who had been standing by and keeping an eye on the boys, said, "No need to apologize. Looks to me like he had it coming."

This made Bryce even angrier. "Man, I'm outta here," he said, walking away from the group. "Brandi, we are done," he shouted back at her.

"Tilt that head back. The bleeding will stop," Matthew said, making fun of Bryce.

Brandi would always have a place in Matthew's heart. She had been his girlfriend through middle school. After she was abducted the previous school year, he swore in his heart that he would look out for her.

He had to make it up to her because he had ruined their relationship by cheating on her. And he didn't do much better freshman year when he tried to date Marisa. She had forgiven him for a lot.

The Haywoods all thanked Matthew, who felt like a hero.

"It was nothing. I'm just glad I could help," Matthew said bashfully.

By the time that drama was over, they were ready to leave. "Mom, can I talk to Matt for a second?"

"Sure, baby. We'll be in the car. And, Matthew," Mrs. Haywood said, "thanks again."

Brandi turned to Matthew when her parents were out of listening range. "You really didn't have to do that."

"You mad at me?"

"Of course not. Bryce is a jerk. I was kind of trying to get rid of him. He was great one minute, awful the next. You know I'm bad with good-bye, though. You saw how long it took me to break up with your cheating behind," she snickered.

"Aw, I wasn't that bad," he said. She looked at him doubtfully. "Okay, maybe I was," he agreed.

"And you still are, but you know I love you, right?" He shook his head and looked down. She tilted his chin so she could look in his eyes. "Always will," she said. "Always will," she said, giving him a kiss on the cheek. "Hey, I gotta go. You know Raven is gonna be talking about you all day. She misses you."

"I miss all of you. Especially you, B. I wish ... I wish I—

"Matt, don't go there. We are much better as friends."

"I know. I know. Just take care of yourself so I won't have to make nobody else bleed."

"Fair enough," she said, laughing as she headed off to the car.

CHAPTER 12

The Fundraiser

Join us at five as Fox News reporter Macey McMillan sits down with the former mistress of Area Fourteen council member hopeful Brian Foster. It's a must-see interview," the reporter announced from the TV screen. Mrs. Foster had a look of irritation and distaste as she passed by the television. She grabbed the remote and clicked it off.

"I don't want to hear that garbage," she told her daughters. "And you shouldn't want to either."

"Well, I want to know what that

hoochie is saying about Dad," Shane said. "And you two are acting like she's just going to go away. She's *not* just going to go away.

"And what about the girl? I looked up her Friender page. She's cute, but she better not be my sister. Her mama need to go on one of those talk shows and find her real baby daddy," Shane continued, disgusted by this woman tainting her father's name.

"I can't believe that she's doing interviews," Robin, who was equally outraged, added.

"Nobody outside of Port City is watching her. She's getting like five minutes of fame instead of fifteen. I'm not worrying about that opportunist. You hear about women coming forward all the time, telling all of their business for some camera time, and then you never hear about them again. I'm sure the same thing will happen with that woman too, and we can go back to our normal, boring life."

"You sure are taking this well," Robin said, suspicious of her mother's behavior.

"Don't think I'm not furious with your father. Because I am. We're going to be working on trust for quite some time. But you don't just throw it all away. At least I don't," Mrs. Foster said.

"Besides, we want to stay married. And you can't do that if you hold a grudge. My grandmother used to tell me that. Funny, but I never knew what she meant until now."

This was not a topic Mrs. Foster wanted to continue. "Enough of this," she declared. "I'm going to need you girls to help out at the fundraiser tomorrow. Robin, can Gavin watch Aiden?"

"No, Gavin's going to help too. His mom said she would watch Aiden."

"Okay, well, Mrs. Maldonado has her team ready to go. Are Marisa and Brandi going to be there?"

"Mom, you know they are."

"I have some of my girls from the college who are coming out to help too," Robin told her.

"I am so ready to get tomorrow over with. That woman's accusations are making us work a lot harder for campaign contributions. Until the DNA test results come back and are revealed, it's just words. I guess people don't know what to believe; they sure aren't sending checks anymore, I know that.

"We need more radio ads and bill-boards. Stringer's face is all over Port City. We have to get your dad more exposure. This fundraiser has to be a success. So much to do, so little time." Their mother went upstairs to continue planning for the next day. She still had a lot to do for the fundraiser.

"You did tape that lady's interview, right?" Shane asked her sister.

"You know I did." Robin laughed. "You

and I are not about to be caught walking around clueless while people are laughing at us."

The next day they were at the park bright and early setting up for the fund-raiser. They placed a banner at the entrance to the park that had a large picture of Mr. Foster on it. The banner read, "When you want honest and fair, Brian Foster will be there."

Because of the wording of the campaign slogan, his opponent jumped on the opportunity to point out that his dishonesty in his marriage would carry over into his work. "If his wife can't trust him, how can the citizens of Port City!" he shouted to his supporters during his rallies. The infidelity issue had taken on a life of its own.

The campaign needed more money, which it had been bleeding since the negative ads began. Hopefully the fund-raiser would be successful. There were bounce houses for the kids and food carts everywhere.

The Maldonados were in one booth selling tamales and tacos with home-made guacamole, salsa, and tortillas. The Haywoods were in another booth selling smoked boudin, turkey legs, and links on a bun. The Foster family was focused on interacting with as many people in the community as possible.

Halfway through the event, they ran out of food and had to resupply their carts. It seemed like the whole community was there cheering on Mr. Foster. The nega-tive press had been so hateful that after momentarily questioning his integrity, the voters returned to support him in full force.

The girls decided to meet up at four to finally take a much-needed break. They had been pulled in every direction all day and knew that the cleanup was going to be a beast. A break just before cleanup was the best time to sneak off for some girl time.

"See, I wouldn't mind hitting a blunt right now," Shane said, relaxing her feet after being on them all day. "I'm exhausted, and this drama with my dad and the other woman is stressing me out."

"I *wish* I would see a blunt in your hand after what we went through with your high yellow behind last year," Brandi warned her.

"For reals," Marisa said, agreeing with her. "Don't even play like that."

"It was a joke. Ha-ha. You know you two should lighten up some. I can't get down like that anymore. Daddy would kill me. It would be on the front page of the *Messenger* tomorrow," she laughed.

"Still not funny," Brandi told her. "What if I was joking about some guy I was dating that I met on the Internet? Would you find it funny?"

"Touché," Shane responded. "So, did y'all have fun today?" She was hoping her family hadn't worked her friends too hard.

"Girl, I had a *good* time! Oh, except when Bryce's creepy self came by." Brandi made a face. "Seriously, I can't be with that dude anymore," she said. "Plus, I can tell he's super angry since Matt put him in his place the other day."

"That story was hilarious. Go, Mattie!" Marisa cheered him on. She turned her attention back to Shane, "Seriously, everybody was here supporting your dad: Mrs. Monroe, Ashton, Trent, the principal ..."

"Ryan stopped by to see me, and Riley came too. I guess that's why I was talking about weed. She's a trigger for me. Remember, she was my li'l smoking buddy back in the gap."

"Shane, shut it!" Brandi spat, slugging her friend good. She was tired of hearing about the good ole days with Riley. They were the ones picking her up when Riley was helping her fall.

"I can't believe that Brendon Cooper came. Y'all remember that guy who dropped my butt on the side of the road. I didn't even wanna speak to him and his li'l crew. He's lucky I was selling links for your dad so I couldn't go ham on him."

"I was happy to see Hayley and Christina. Even Ashley came by to get tacos. I'm telling you, everyone in Port City was here. I think your dad's got this in the bag. Councilman Stringer better look out," Marisa announced. "Hey, let's go get this park cleaned up. I see Mama looking for me."

"Where are all those people we named? We should have recruited some help," Brandi announced.

"We'll be done in no time," Marisa told them. "Come on, let's get it over with."

What would I do without my girls? Shane thought. *I'm so lucky to have them.*

CHAPTER 13

Shane

Mr. Foster's city council campaign seemed to be making time fly. Every day the family had to participate in some event—sometimes there was more than one! Most days, as soon as Shane got home from school, she was picking out clothing to go to a party, a fundraiser, a press conference, or a photo opportunity. That was only the tip of the iceberg for the Foster family.

Tonight was no different. They were invited to yet another event. This one was taking place at God's People Church. They weren't members of the church, but Shane had visited there a few times. Tonight's event showcased up-and-coming gospel artists in the area. Mr. Foster thought that it would be a good opportunity for the family to go out and mingle with more people.

"I don't understand why you have to drag us to all of these stupid events. Robin and I aren't running for anything. You and Mom can go alone. It's Friday night, and I don't want to spend it with a whole bunch of church people I don't know."

"You better stop complaining and get dressed. I really don't feel like hearing any drama, Shane," her father warned.

"Hey, why don't you and Robin go to the mall and get something to wear," her mother suggested. "Just take Daddy's card. I'll watch Aiden."

"See? Mom speaks my language."

"It's my money she's offering up. I don't get any credit?" He sounded stern, but her dad was smiling as he said it.

"Nope," Shane said, kissing her mom on the cheek and running to tell Robin.

It took forever for her sister to get ready. First Aiden started to cry, then she had to get his bottles ready, and then she wanted to make sure that there were enough diapers.

"Come on," Shane complained after waiting for twenty minutes.

"Girl, I have to make sure my little man is good before I leave. You'll understand one day."

They hit the mall armed and ready with their dad's plastic. First it was Gap, American Eagle, and Forever 21. Then on to T.J. Maxx for some real bargains. They were sure they'd maxed out their father's credit card. They'd even done some damage at the makeup counter.

By the time they'd left, they had purchased outfits for the night's event and entire new spring wardrobes. Good-bye to those dark winter colors, and hello to the coral, orange, sage, and white hues of a lovely Texas spring.

They even went a little crazy shopping for baby boy clothes. Aiden totally scored, not that he would ever know. They'd grabbed a few polo shirts, plaid shorts, and tiny topsiders for him.

They looked at each other on the ride home and giggled nervously. It felt good to get back at their father just a little bit. A little devilish. He deserved a little pain in the wallet.

Both Shane and Robin looked great in the new outfits they had purchased for the God's People event that evening. They were both ready for spring.

By the time the whole family was dressed and ready to go, the event had been going on for thirty minutes. "We are late. I hate being late," her mother complained.

"Mom, I don't just have to get myself ready. I have to think about Aiden too."

"I know, baby, but that means you need to start earlier."

"Or you need to help more."

"Here we go with that again—"

"Hey, Foster women, chill out. I have enough on my mind right now. I don't need upheaval in my home too," Mr. Foster interrupted.

When they arrived, they were ushered to a table that had been designated for their family. Many of the other people running for city council had already arrived. The Foster family took their seats and sat back to enjoy the music.

The food was being served simultaneously with the performances. Dinner and gospel music—it mixed well. When Shane got up to refill their drinks, she was surprised to see Ryan Petry there. "What are you doing here?"

"This is my church. What are you doing here?" he asked.

"Gotta support the fam. You don't

strike me as the churchgoing type, I have to say."

"Well, you don't either," he said matter-of-factly.

"Well, I am. Hey, let me drop these drinks off at our table, and then we can catch up."

Shane and Ryan stepped outside to talk. She enjoyed his company. The air between them was so easy at times, but he was leaving in just four months for college. Shane was no fool. She wasn't about to get involved with a senior and set herself up for heartbreak.

"When are you going to let me take you out again?" he asked.

"I'm not."

"Why? I know you want to."

"You're leaving for college, Ryan. I'm sure you'll meet a lot of girls like me, beautiful, smart, cool ... well, maybe not."

"Definitely not," he said, moving closer to her.

Shane could feel her heart beating. The closer he came, the harder it was to breathe. When someone burst through of the door, it startled the two of them. It was her father.

"You swore you would keep them out of this. I will not have my girls ridiculed. They're going through enough as it is with the Sasha situation. You fix this or else I'm out of this race!" he screamed into the phone.

He turned to go back into the building, but Shane stopped him. "Dad?"

"Oh, Shane, what are you doing out here? Hi, Ryan," he said, shaking Ryan's hand and trying to calm himself down.

"What was that about, Dad?" she asked.

"Nothing, baby, nothing for you to worry about."

Shane was nervous. She heard what her father had said, but she didn't want to press him. It wasn't the time or the place, and she knew it. They all went back inside together.

"Pick up where we left off later?" Ryan whispered to her as his lips grazed the back of her neck.

Chills ran down her spine, and she tingled all over. The butterflies in her stomach started to dance. She had to run from him. The last thing she expected was to find herself attracted to Ryan Petry. This had come out of nowhere, and she wanted it to stop.

She took her seat next to Robin and grabbed Aiden, who was squirming all over the place. The loud music was interrupting what would have been his bedtime.

Robin went on a much-needed rest-room break. Shane was not surprised that her mother hadn't taken Aiden from Robin. She talked a good game about helping them more, but it just wasn't who she was. She was getting better, but she still had a way to go.

When they got into the car, no one uttered a word. Shane wanted to know what her father was talking about on the phone, but he wasn't saying anything, and Shane was a little afraid to bring it up. She didn't know what to do.

Her mother could sense that something was wrong. She reached out to touch her husband's hand. "Is everything okay?"

"Yeah, I just have a lot on my mind," he told her.

"Maybe it's what you were yelling about on your phone," Shane mumbled.

"Let it go, Shane," he said. Then his phone started ringing. He quickly picked it up. "That's not okay. ... And we can't do anything about it? ... Well, I'm not running anymore. ... This is over, Clyde. I'm done. ... No, I won't think about this," he said, hanging up the phone abruptly.

"What, Brian? What happened now?" Mrs. Foster pushed.

"Not now," he whispered to his wife.

He turned his face away. But then Mr. Foster took a deep breath, turned back toward his family, and began to speak. He had some devastating news to share with them. "There's another article being posted in the *Messenger* tomorrow."

"What did you do now?" Mrs. Foster asked him automatically, taking her hand away from his.

"Nothing, it's, um ..." he hesitated, "it's about the girls."

"What?!" Robin shouted.

"There's going to be an article in the *Messenger* tomorrow. They found out about Shane's brief visit to rehab last year, and they are going to write about it. Robin, they have you painted in a negative light because of Aiden."

"Dad, you have to do something," Shane demanded.

"I can't stop them from running the article. I've already tried. The owner of the *Messenger* is good friends with Stringer.

It's all politics, baby girl. My hands are tied. Even if I drop out of the race, it's too late. They are definitely printing the article."

When they pulled up at the house, it was mayhem. They were all angry and taking it out on each other.

Robin and Shane were mortified that their lives were about to be on display for all of Port City to see. They took their frustrations out on their father, even though they knew if he could have sheltered them from this humiliation, he would have. There was nothing they could do but wait for the paper to come out in the morning. No amount of yelling could stop the inevitable.

The next day, Mr. Foster was up bright and early to go to the corner store to purchase four copies of the *Messenger*. But when he opened the front door, there were ten copies on their front porch. He could see the family picture they had taken at Christmas right in the middle of the page.

His heart dropped as he bent down to pick up the papers. He looked around to see if the person who left them was still around, but there was no movement on the street.

He sat alone in his office to read the article. It made him sick. The article concluded, "How can he lead a city when his home is this dysfunctional?"

They painted a picture of Shane as a pot-smoking, pill-popping sophomore who could not be controlled. Robin was portrayed as a promiscuous teenager, who once showed great promise but threw it all away to chase after boys.

Mr. Foster knew that his daughters were going to be hurt and embarrassed—and angry. He felt that it was his fault, and he had to figure out a way to soften the blows.

"Clyde, it's me. Did you read the article yet? ... Well, as my campaign manager, I would think you would have been up at the crack of dawn trying to get a copy too. ... No, Clyde, I'm not going to ignore it. It's not about me, it's about my girls. ... You know what, you're fired. I'm going to handle my own PR." Mr. Foster was livid. He wanted to blame somebody. He knew it wasn't Clyde's fault, but he was angry.

Mr. Foster sat back to reflect on what had taken place. He had to show the girls the article. It was time for another family meeting.

As they all gathered around the breakfast table, their father handed each of them their own copy of the paper. He could see the shock on their faces as they read the article detailing their lives. He had to keep his composure. They had to believe he had all of this under control.

"This is a joke, right?" Robin asked in disbelief. Mr. Foster shook his head. "I can't believe that this is in the paper. I sound like a slut." She read it again. "I am not promiscuous. I've been with Gavin forever. We plan on getting married and everything. I'm suing the *Messenger*!" Robin was livid.

Shane sat there sipping hot chocolate. Her blank stare alarmed her parents. "Shane!" her mother yelled. "Snap out of it."

"I can't blame anyone but myself," she said calmly, not wanting to meet her father's gaze. Tears welled up in her eyes. "I know that my behavior has hurt you, and I'm sorry." The tears she was trying to fight began to fall down her cheeks. It was a much different reaction than her father had anticipated.

"Don't feel bad, baby. This family has borne the brunt of all of the negative press that's been thrown our way, but we are tough. How about we fight back?" he asked, more hopeful than ever before.

"Now, you're speaking my language," Mrs. Foster said, ready to fight for her family. "Nobody talks about my babies like that!"

Mr. Foster called a press conference at City Hall that same day.

They were all there, including Aiden and Gavin. Mr. Foster had called all of the major news outlets to come. "My opponent, Mr. Stringer, would have you think that all families are perfect, but they aren't, and neither is his. But I am *not* going to stoop to his level and put all of his dirty laundry on the front page of the newspaper. Instead, I want to reintroduce you to my family."

He pointed out each of them and said their names. "We are broken, yet fixable. We have all made mistakes, but still we stand. Our family is much like Port City, perfect and flawed at the same time. If you look at my girls, you see beauty and hope in their eyes, even though we have made mistakes.

"That is what the Foster family will bring back to this town, the ability to see a mistake and make it right, and not just gloss over the problem. Mr. Stringer believes in glossing over problems in his family and his city. I believe in facing them head-on, which is why I had the DNA test."

There was a hush in the crowd. "And the results are in. That little girl is one hundred percent not my child. I feel sorry for her. Her mother and Mr. Stringer used her as a pawn in their little game.

"That mean-spirited behavior is what Stringer is known for. He doesn't care who gets hurt as long as he gets what he wants. He believes what he's doing works for this city, and I'm here to tell you that it doesn't.

"I want to show you what a councilman who cares about your city can do. I will work until Port City is a replica of the one that I called home many years ago." Mr. Foster paused. "Mr. Stringer, this message is for you," he said, pointing to the cameras. "If you think dragging my family through the mud will deter me from helping this city, then you have another thing coming." The crowd went wild. As they cheered, he concluded, "Brian Foster, Area Fourteen ... get out and vote! Thank you for coming out."

Those who supported the Foster family cheered excitedly. The news reporters began to pan the crowd for live shots to add to the evening news. When it aired on the news stations, all of the wonderful things that Mr. Foster said were taken out. The only thing left was the message to Mr. Stringer, who refused to comment.

In the *Port City Tribune*, Mr. Foster's speech was very detailed and well-documented. The newspaper didn't just have sound bites, it had it all. Their family had been vindicated that day, and the Foster name was intact. With very few days left until voting day, the campaign was stronger than ever.

CHAPTER 14

Marisa

The Maldonados were a family in transition. Mr. Maldonado was having a hard time recovering from the time he spent in jail because of his courtroom outbursts—which had almost got him deported as well.

Making matters worse, the family was experiencing a financial crunch. Mr. Maldonado had always been the family's primary breadwinner, but his once lucrative construction business was bleeding money because he had been away for too long.

While he was in jail, there was no one to generate new business or give estimates to potential customers. And the customers he did have weren't completely happy with the service they received while Mr. Maldonado was away.

When he was released from custody, he discovered that some of his customers had moved on to other companies. So months later, Mr. Maldonado found himself doing what he could to rebuild his business—and his reputation.

Luckily, Marisa's modeling career had taken off since her first shoot with Gap. Not only had Gap asked her to do another campaign for their multicultural ads, but her new agent, Marcie Miller, was putting her to work. Marcie had approached her during that first shoot and their relationship took off. She proved that she believed in Marisa.

After her Gap shoot, she had been booked for a Ford Focus ad. When the local advertisers in Houston were sent her photos and cover letter, she got their attention. She was a fresh face who they felt would appeal to the growing Hispanic community. She had only been modeling for a little over a month, but people were starting to know who she was.

The morning of her third shoot in Houston was a struggle for Marisa. She gathered the items she needed, her backpack, water bottle, pillow and blanket for the car, and her tablet to read the novel she had downloaded. It was still four in the morning, and they had a long ride ahead.

"Let's go, mi hija. You are going to be late," her mom said, like she had already been up for hours.

"Mom, it's four in the morning. How can anybody be late if they are ready to go at four. We will be okay."

"Your call time is at six. It takes two hours to get to Houston. You do the math."

Marisa rolled her eyes. She knew she

shouldn't be mean to her mother. Mrs. Maldonado was rearranging her schedule to be the chauffeur. She realized how important modeling was to her daughter.

Marisa was tired and grumpy, but she knew she could catch some z's in the car. No way could she go on set with dark circles under her eyes. So she tried to make the best of the situation. Everyone was counting on her.

Armed with a water bottle at all times, Marisa took a big gulp. When she drank a lot of water, her skin seems to glow, and that hydration translated in her photographs. She seemed to explode off the page.

Everything mattered now. She was supporting her family. Modeling seemed to be a full-time job.

She slept all the way to Houston. When she arrived on set, they were ready for her in hair and makeup. She tried to do her homework so she would be prepared for school the next day, but it was hard. The stylists were constantly asking her to turn her head, look this way, close her eyes. She gave up on her assignments and focused on the shoot.

She couldn't get her Monday night homework done, but she knew if she could nail the photo shoot, then her career would move even further ahead. Her agent called when she was done to let her know how happy the Ford reps were with the pictures. They wanted to work with her again. Marisa was ecstatic.

"Did you get your homework done?" her mother asked when they were on I-10.

"I tried, Mama, but it was too much."

"Well, take your books out and start now."

"I'm too tired now. I can't focus on Shakespeare or numbers, forget about it."

"Marisa, your father and I only agreed

to this because you said that you would keep up with your schoolwork. So make sure you do that. Now get some rest on the drive home so you can get your work done later."

Marisa reclined her seat and dozed off. Modeling was physically and mentally draining. She had always known it was hard work, and she enjoyed every minute, but she never knew how much it would exhaust her.

When she got back, it was still early. They finished shooting by one o'clock, and they were back in Port City by three. Marisa was missing her friends, so she decided to get dropped off at PCH instead of going home.

"Being at the school will help me focus. I'm going straight to the library," she promised, jumping out of the car. She got to the school when the last bell was about to ring. She went to Shane's locker to wait for her two best friends.

"Mari!" Shane shouted when she saw her. "You're here. How was work?"

"Good and tiring, but I slept in the car."

"America's Next Top Model decided to pay us common folk a visit," Brandi teased her when she got to the lockers.

"You and your jokes," Marisa retorted, turning her mouth up with a small smirk. "Y'all seen Trent anywhere? I'm missing him too."

Out of nowhere Trent appeared in the hallway. He had four freshman cheerleaders smiling up at him like he was a god or something. They were hanging on his every word, and he looked to be enjoying the attention.

"Baby in the building," he said as soon as he laid eyes on Marisa. He grabbed her and hugged her tightly. "How was work, Mari? You came back early to see me?"

"Yeah," she said stiffly.

"What's wrong?" She didn't answer. He turned to Brandi and Shane. "What's up with your girl? Why she giving me the cold shoulder?" They both shrugged, trying to stay out of their drama. They loved Trent, but their loyalties were always with their girl.

"Who are they?" she asked, pointing to the four cheerleaders standing behind Trent.

"Oh, they are my locker girls for basketball season."

"Four locker girls, Trent, really?"

"Brandi should be your locker girl, not them."

Brandi leaned in to Marisa, "Um, not going to happen. I'm not catering to my best friend's man. There's something just wrong with that."

"Well, I don't like it."

"Don't make a scene. Let's just talk later," he whispered.

Brandi looked at the freshmen who had been assigned to Trent and motioned for them to move along.

"Whatever," their leader said, mouthing off. "Bye, Trent. We'll talk later."

"Bye, Trent," the other three said in unison.

"Bye, ladies," he said, smiling and making the girls giggle. Marisa wanted to control herself in front of them, but she punched him in the arm as his gaze fell to their backsides when they walked away.

"You make me sick," she told him, disgusted.

"Girl, I'm a man. I can look, but I promise I won't touch."

"Um-hm, tell me anything. I'm breaking up with you when you go to college. Keep it up."

"Girl, you gonna marry me," he said, picking her up and cradling her in his huge arms. "You think I'm crazy enough to let you go. I'm poppin' bottles with models."

"Boy put me down before you drop me," she demanded.

They heard someone clear their throat

behind them, it was the principal, Mrs. Montgomery. "That's enough, you two. Marisa, were you even in school today?"

"No, ma'am," she said, embarrassed that Trent still had her off her feet. She was talking to Principal Montgomery from the sky.

"And here you are causing all these problems in the hall. Trent, will you please put Marisa down? Trent, you go to practice. Marisa, I need to talk to you."

Marisa's heart dropped. The last thing she wanted to do was sit and talk to Mrs. Montgomery. She wasn't mean or anything, but she was the principal. "Let's go to my office," she suggested.

Marisa turned to Shane and Brandi. "I'll catch up with y'all when I'm done," she told them.

Once they were in the principal's office, Marisa became even more uncomfortable. Mrs. Montgomery took her seat at her gigantic desk and was looking down at Marisa. Marisa squirmed under the principal's gaze.

"Some of your teachers have voiced some concerns about your grades since your modeling jobs started. You are such a good student, Marisa. I would hate for you to fall too far behind."

"I'm trying, Mrs. Montgomery. I really am," she whined.

"I know, but I sat with you and your mom, and I agreed to let you take your work with you to Houston. She assured me that you were going to be able to handle working and school. Now here we are, nearly a month later, and some of your homework has been less than stellar. And you didn't do so well on your math midterm."

Marisa's head fell to her chest. "It's so hard to study when I'm in hair and makeup. I have to have a clear head when I shoot. I sleep on the way there and on the way back because I'm so tired. I don't know how to get it all done." She started to cry.

"It's okay. It's a brand new experience, but you have to adjust because if you don't, you will fail your classes."

Marisa had never made an F on her report card. She knew she had to pull it together. She thanked Mrs. Montgomery and left her office.

When she told Brandi and Shane her dilemma, they vowed to help. They had the same teachers and knew how important modeling was to Marisa's family right now. It wasn't like she could just give up on it. The Maldonados needed the money. They decided to head over to Jerry's to get Marisa caught up and eat some good burgers at the same time.

"Hey, I'm buying," she told them. "I'm cashing Gap checks now."

"Hook a sista up, then," Brandi told her.

"That's what I'm talking about. Free food courtesy of the Gap," Shane agreed.

They ate, they worked, and they laughed. "Good friends are so hard to find, and I found two," Marisa told her friends as they gathered their belongings. It had been a long day, but she did everything that she was supposed to do for work and school, and it just felt good.

CHAPTER 15

Brandi

$\mathcal{C}$an I puleez come c u," Bryce texted. Normally, breaking up was hard for her, but this time it had been easy. Her father's presence back in her life had an impact on how she saw relationships. Her self-worth had returned. She was feeling like the Brandi from middle school who had just made cheerleader, who had just started dating Matthew Kincade—the best football player at Central Middle School.

If Bryce had sent that text to Brandi last year or even last semester, she would have probably given in. He didn't notice that she had changed. It happened so gradually, Brandi barely noticed it herself. But she *had* changed.

After a string of bad relationships, Brandi knew it was time to get strong. After Matthew cheated on her, she felt ruined. He started liking Marisa around the same time that she realized her father was falling further into his addiction. Then she met Brendon, who was a loser— on the football team and in life.

And then there was Camden, who turned out to be a stalker named Steven.

Now Bryce had to be added to the list of bad relationship choices. She knew one thing, she was never going to ignore red flags again or try to dismiss her internal early warning signs. She was done going down that road. No text was going to stop that.

Her father's recovery and presence was a huge part of her new outlook on her life and relationships. Whenever she thought of her dad now, she smiled, and her smiles felt genuine again. It hadn't been like that in a long time.

The night before, her father had taken her out on a date. It used to be a ritual with the two of them, but once his addiction got really bad, it was over. They were trying to get back to where they had once been.

He was working, and he wasn't wasting his money on drugs or stealing her mom's money. Their finances were better, so they had more money to enjoy each other. They could go out to eat more. They went shopping on Saturdays like they used to do. Life was good.

The doorbell startled Brandi out of her thoughts. Her father was at the door before she could make it down the stairs.

"Is Brandi home?" she heard Bryce's voice ask her father.

"Bran!" her father's voice was tense. "Bryce is here."

Hasn't he been paying attention? I'm done with this guy, she thought.

She stood at the top of the stairs. Her eyes told her father that she wasn't coming down. He turned back to Bryce. "I don't think Brandi wants to see you right now, Bryce. And frankly, I don't want to see you either. If you ever lay your hands on my daughter again, I will be after you faster than you—"

"Daddy!" Brandi hollered.

"Brandi!" Bryce yelled. "I'm sorry. I should never have blown up like that. You know I need you. Please don't do this."

"It's over, Bryce! Go home!" She wasn't budging.

"It's not over. I won't let you go! I can't!"

Her father grabbed Bryce by the neck and threw him against the door.

"Stop!" Brandi gasped, running down the stairs. She didn't want to be with Bryce, but she didn't want her dad to hurt him either.

"My daughter's done with you! You got that, kid!"

"Get yo' hands off me, old man, fo' I have to hurt you."

Brandi was trying to pry his fingers from Bryce's throat. "Stop it, Daddy."

"Don't let me catch you bothering my daughter again. You got that?"

By this time, Bryce was turning red. He could barely speak. His smart mouth was gone. "Yes, sir. I'll leave her alone."

Brandi watched as her father let him go. Bryce coughed, and tried to regain his composure and dignity. He turned and walked away. Brandi's father shut the door and faced his daughter.

Brandi had people on her side now. First Matthew had saved her from this creep and now her father. She knew that if there was a next time, she might not be so lucky. She knew that it was time for her to be alone. No more dating. No more boys.

"You have to be more careful in who

you choose to date, Bran," her father warned.

"You know what, Dad? I had a good time on our date last night. Maybe that's my kind of dating for right now."

James Haywood smiled. He knew that his sobriety was having a positive effect on his daughter, and he was pleased. "Sounds good to me," he said, hugging her. "Now go get Raven. I want to take you both out tonight."

"I'm right here," Raven said, eavesdropping from the stairs. They both laughed. It was classic Raven to be in everybody's business. "You know I have to make sure you're okay, B. You're my rock," she told her big sister, slipping on her flip-flops.

"Don't tell anybody, but you're mine too," she told her little sister. She picked Raven up and headed to the car.

Her father watched his two girls as he

locked up the house. *Thank God I'm home,* he thought. *Cat always had to work to keep us afloat. Well, I'm done with that. I need to man up. Thank God I'm home.*

CHAPTER 16

The Votes Are In

The Foster home was packed with guests for the election night party. It had already been a crazy day. Everyone had worked at the polls for twelve hours. Mrs. Foster and Mrs. Maldonado were at the house preparing to feed everyone.

Mr. Foster was happy that Clyde had agreed to return to the campaign. He had fired him in a fit of anger over the newspaper article that criticized his daughters.

Once he cooled off, he acknowledged that Clyde couldn't have stopped the article. He sincerely apologized and asked him to come back.

Brandi enlisted help from the cheerleading squad. They were passing out stickers and pamphlets at supermarkets that detailed Mr. Foster's vision for the city. The twirlers had accompanied Marisa to polling locations across town, doing much of the same.

People wearing red, white, and blue *Foster for Fourteen* T-shirts swarmed the parking lots of both the public library and City Hall. Brian Foster was strategically working both locations while Clyde provided drinks and food for the workers.

"I'll be glad when this is over," Mr. Foster had admitted to his wife at noon when she stopped by to bring lunch for the campaign workers.

Mrs. Foster had many hats to wear throughout Election Day. First she had to alter larger-size T-shirts so they would attractively fit the tiny twirlers and cheerleaders. They had run out of extra-small shirts weeks ago. Luckily Shane and Robin were able to help their mom out.

On election morning, Mrs. Foster regretted not having Clyde order more T-shirts—in any size. When Shane told her there were twenty more girls who needed shirts, she ran to Walmart and purchased plain white Ts and iron-ons. There was a bit of trial and error, but finally, all of the girls had *Foster for Fourteen* across their shirts.

By the time everyone was in place, it was time to organize lunches. Then there was the dinner she would serve everyone once it was over. Mrs. Foster worked like a machine. Her nervous energy wouldn't let her sit for even a minute.

As she buzzed around Lupe Maldonado, waiting for their guests to arrive, Kim Foster was a ball of nerves. Mrs.

Maldonado gently touched her hand. "It's going to be okay. Brian has this."

"You just never know. Sometimes I wish he would have never agreed to do this. It's taken such a toll on the girls. Well, whatever happens, happens."

"Kim, your husband agreed to run for office to save my family. You know if George had never got into all that trouble in court, we wouldn't be having this conversation. Brian saved him. I know it's been tough for you all, and I'm sorry."

Kim turned to Lupe with tears in her eyes. It had been an emotional ride. "You don't ever have to be sorry. We would make the same decision if it happened again. There was no way that we could let George get deported, not after all he's done for this community. It wouldn't have been right."

"This is like a destiny thing, Kim. It was just supposed to be. This city needs

Brian. I'm telling you. It'll all be worth it in the end."

"What are you two in here babbling about?" Brian asked, walking through the door.

Kim wiped the tears from her face. "Did the polls close already?"

"They are closing. Are you okay?" he asked, concerned.

"Yes, baby," she said, kissing her husband gently. "It was just girl talk. Nothing for you to worry about."

The rest of the workers were close behind Mr. Foster. As they began to file into the house, one thing was for sure, they had worked up their appetites. Even though they had been at the polling stations all day, the ladies started to serve the hungry volunteers, who were watching the returns as they rolled in.

It wasn't looking good for the Foster campaign. The only numbers that had been calculated were those ballots that had been mailed. Stringer was in the lead, holding sixty-five percent of the vote.

Kim left the other ladies and joined her husband when the numbers came in for Port City. "This is nerve-wracking. If we don't win, I'm done with politics forever."

"Yeah, me too," he admitted. "This was more than I bargained for."

"Daddy, don't worry about the mail-in ballots," Shane said, listening to her parents' conversation. "I just know you have this."

One of the campaign workers chimed in, "You know Stringer padded those mail-in ballots. They've been doing it for years. The real numbers are coming soon."

The volunteer was right. The first polling location returns were reported. Everything changed. Mr. Foster was still behind with forty-seven percent of the vote, but he was closing in on his opponent.

Mrs. Foster began pouring a Texas-label sparkling wine for the final count.

"Come on, come on," Robin said impatiently.

Port City was one of the last cities because they were listed alphabetically. Everyone in the room was on the edge of their seats.

All of the surrounding cities had their final numbers, so they knew that Port City's numbers would be in too. And there it was, "Brian Foster, Area 14, 55% ..."

Everyone in the Foster house went wild. The teenagers were jumping up and down; they had been a part of something bigger than themselves. The adults were shaking Brian's hand and congratulating him. "You're just what this city needs," they told him.

Mrs. Foster cried, hugging Aiden. "We did it, little person," she said, kissing her grandchild.

Shane and Robin cried. It had been

physically and emotionally draining, but they did it.

Mr. Foster's phone vibrated in his pocket. It was Stringer. He congratulated him on a race well ran. His time representing Area 14 was over, but Mr. Foster knew that Stringer would always be there waiting for the next election. He was just that type.

After the numbers were revealed, the news reporters started giving comments about the winners. It was unanimous that the biggest upset was Area 14's, where the incumbent had lost to a first-time candidate. "Brian Foster's speech at City Hall probably put the nail in the coffin for Councilman Stringer," she said, playing a clip from that day. "Mr. Stringer was not available for comment."

Shane found her girls in the sea of people that crowded into their downstairs. "Hey, come upstairs with me," she told them. When they got to her room, she turned to them with tears in her eyes. "Thank you for everything. I couldn't have made it through this without you."

"You know we'll always have your back," Brandi told her.

Marisa shook her head in agreement. "I'm just glad that he won. All of his hard work paid off."

"So you think Mrs. Smith will let you turn all your science assignments in late now that you're dad's a council member?" Brandi teased.

"Yeah, and maybe you'll get a reserved table at Jerry's since you're famous now," Marisa said, joining in on the fun. "Maybe Robin'll get her own parking space!"

Shane smiled and shook her head at her two friends.

Project Graduation

I can't get you into Project Graduation," Shane told Marisa and Brandi. They begged to assist her with the photography she had been assigned to do for the senior class. The senior class party was strictly off limits to anyone without an invitation.

"But this is Trent's last day as a Port City High Wildcat, and I have to spend it with him. You have to need help with *something*," Marisa whined.

"And I just wanna go," Brandi told her. "I'm bored."

"You two are impossible. The seniors don't want to celebrate with under-classmen. That will ruin the night for them."

"We could wear disguises," Brandi said, picking up the Mardi Gras mask that they had worn in the parade.

"Oh, I like that idea," Marisa told them. "Disguises!"

"Y'all dumb. That's a horrible idea, but let me call Mrs. Monroe and see what I can do." Shane made a call and detailed all of the equipment and shots that she needed to take for the senior class. She explained to Mrs. Monroe how difficult her job was going to be, and she requested two assis-tants. Mrs. Monroe told her to give the other team members a call and see if they could help her.

"It seems that everyone is gone already for some trip or other. I've tried calling several people from our team. Is it possible that Marisa and Brandi could help me? They've worked with me a lot before on personal shoots, so they know what needs to be done. They'll be really helpful, I promise."

"That's a wonderful idea, Shane. I'll just let Mrs. Montgomery know that they'll be accompanying you. Have fun and work hard."

"Thanks, Mrs. Monroe."

Marisa and Brandi were as eager as five-year-olds on Halloween. As soon as she hung up the phone, they pounced on her. "We knew you could come up with something!" Brandi told her.

"You are my girl, for real!" shouted Marisa.

"Yeah, yeah, yeah, y'all get dressed 'cause you are helping me for real. Put on all black too. Don't even try to be all fancy. We are there to work."

"Yes, ma'am," Brandi said smartly.

"I'll call my mom right now to bring my clothes."

"Me too," Marisa told her.

By the time they left, they looked artistic and hip. "I could get used to this look," Brandi told Shane, looking in the mirror seductively. "Let me see your camera."

"No, you're too clumsy. Besides, we've gotta get going. My mom is getting antsy. She's gonna pick us up too, so she wants to get a little sleep."

In the car, Shane ran down their job duties. "B, you can take care of the lighting; Marisa, you can be in charge of positioning people for their pictures. They don't even hire a photographer anymore now that I'm getting my professional on. Plus, I'm free."

They set up for pictures, but they didn't open the booth for another hour. They wanted to get the seniors in action as they indulged in the festivities. There were carnival games with prizes, tables set up for dominoes and card games like gin rummy and hearts, raffles, and food.

The movie was scheduled to play at midnight, and the seniors would be served popcorn and refreshments. Pizza Inn sponsored the event. There was a buffet set up in the cafeteria. Marisa was hard at work when Trent, Ashton, and Dalton arrived. She was helping Shane with shots of students getting pizza and salads from the buffet area.

"What are you doing here?" Trent asked, surprised. They had seen each other at his graduation earlier that day, but she never told him that she was coming tonight.

"I wanted to spend your last night of high school with you, so I'm helping Shane with photography," Marisa said with a sly smile.

"Hey, my future baby mama is here,

everybody, so don't try to get fresh with me tonight," Ashton said, hugging Shane and kissing her on the cheek.

"Boy, move. I'm working. I don't have time to play, Ash."

"Girl, you make time. I'm leaving for the army this summer. You are going to miss me."

"Let me get through the night, and I'll worry about missing you tomorrow."

"You are mean, Shane Foster."

"And you love it," she said, getting back to her work. *Last day of Ashton,* she thought. *You know I hate to say it, but I think I just might miss that fool.*

"And what about me?" Ryan asked. Shane turned around quickly when she heard Ryan's voice.

Shane didn't know what to say. Somewhere inside, she regretted not taking their relationship further. She knew it was a mistake, but she also knew that she would be more hurt saying good-bye. He wasn't the type to stay in Port City. She knew if it was supposed to happen, they would meet again.

"Yeah," she finally said, "I'm going to miss you." Her voice was serious, and he reached out to hold her in his arms.

When he let her go, he went back into boss mode and said, "You're slacking off. Is this what I taught you?"

Shane went back to taking pictures.

The seniors were going to be released after they were served breakfast at six a.m. But Shane, Marisa, and Brandi left at two, after they'd fulfilled their duties.

"Waffle House?" Shane asked them. "My mom said she'd take us. I'm starving and a little depressed."

"Me too," Marisa said, looking out of the window. "There will never be another Trent Walker at Port City High. He was one of a kind. I can't believe he's leaving."

"Arkansas isn't that far away," Brandi said, trying to cheer up her friend.

"Yeah, B. It *is* that far away," Marisa said. She lost it and started crying. "Who am I without him?"

"A friend, a sister, a twirler, an actress, and a model," Shane said, listing Marisa's many accomplishments. "I can't lie. I'm going to miss them too, Ashton and Ryan." That broke the tension in the car. At the same time, they all started laughing.

"Yeah, it has less punch when there's two of them," Brandi told her.

"I know, but it's so hard to choose just one, and now there's none. We're going to be all alone next year." They pulled into the parking lot at Waffle House. "But if we have to be alone, I'm just glad that we'll be alone together."

"Yeah, me too." A small smile appeared on Brandi's face. "Bright side—we are the new junior class."

"Riiight, I hadn't even thought about it. We are upperclassmen now," Marisa said, looking at her friends.

"Ride or die?" Shane asked.

"Ride or die," Brandi and Marisa said together.

ABOUT THE AUTHOR

Shannon Freeman

ℬorn and raised in Port Arthur, Texas, Shannon Freeman works full time as an English teacher in her hometown. After completing college at Oral Roberts University, Freeman began her work in the classroom teaching English and oral communications. At that time, the characters of her breakout series, Port City High, began to form, but these characters would not come to life for years. An apartment fire destroyed almost all of the young teacher's worldly possessions before she could begin writing. With nothing to lose, Freeman packed up and headed to Los Angeles, California, to pursue a passion that burned within her since her youth, the entertainment industry.

Beginning in 2001, Freeman made numerous television appearances and enjoyed a rich life full of friends and hard work. In 2008, her world once again changed when she and her husband, Derrick Freeman, found out that they were expecting their first child. Freeman then made the difficult decision to return to Port Arthur and start the family that she had always wanted.

At that time, Freeman returned to the classroom, but entertaining others was still a desire that could not be quenched. Being in the classroom again inspired her to tell the story of Marisa, Shane, and

Brandi that had been evolving for almost a decade. She began to write and the Port City High series was born.

Port City High is the culmination of Freeman's life experiences, including her travels across the United States and Europe. Her stories reflect the friendships she's made across the globe. Port City High is the next breakout series for today's young adult readers. Freeman says, "The topics are relevant and life changing. I just hope that people are touched by my characters' stories as much as I am."